Wo
People with Learning Disabilities and Offending Behaviour

A handbook

Eddie Chaplin, Jayne Henry and Steve Hardy

Foreword by Nick Bouras

estia centre

Working with People with Learning Disabilities and Offending Behaviour

A handbook

Published by:
Pavilion Publishing (Brighton) Ltd, part of OLM group
Richmond House
Richmond Road
Brighton BN2 3RL
UK
Tel: 01273 623222
Fax: 01273 625526
Email: info@pavpub.com
Web: www.pavpub.com

First published 2009, reprinted 2010

A catalogue record for this book is available from the British Library.

ISBN: 978 1 84196 228 3

Pavilion editor: Grace Fairley (www.thebigwideword.com)
Cover design: Emma Garbutt, Pavilion
Page design and layout: Emma Garbutt, Pavilion
Print: Printfast

Working with People with Learning Disabilities and Offending Behaviour

A handbook

Eddie Chaplin, Jayne Henry and Steve Hardy

Foreword by Nick Bouras

*e*stia centre

Contents

Section 1: Background and overview

Section 2: Legal and ethical

Section 3: Psychopathology and offending

Section 4: Working with offenders

Section 5: Glossaries

Foreword

Forensic issues for people with learning disabilities have attracted a lot of attention in recent years with the implementation of community care programmes. This publication is an important addition to our knowledge in the field and it is exceptionally noteworthy in addressing best practice and training.

Conceptual issues related to the definition of learning disabilities and forensic issues, particularly unreported offending behaviour, complicate the understanding of the association between offending behaviour and learning disabilities. The prevalence of people with learning disabilities and forensic issues varies with laws, social policy and the presence of alternative rehabilitation and support systems in place.

Following deinstitutionalisation, the needs of people with learning disabilities and offending behaviour – some of whom also have additional mental health problems – have been overlooked, in spite of a few innovative community care schemes for some subgroups of people. Service provision has lagged behind developments for local services, resulting in many people with learning disabilities and forensic needs being placed in residential facilities a long way from their local communities, and at times in unnecessary restrictive environments. The lack of training in how to address their needs has contributed to the creation of a vacuum of know-how for this population, with adverse effects on their quality of life. The coexistence of mental health problems for a sizeable number of people with learning disabilities has further exaggerated the problems. Care for people with learning disability and forensic needs requires strong interfaces and partnership between learning disabilities, mental health and forensic services. Such links are still weak and hampered by ideologies, insufficient policies and shortage of resources.

This comprehensive publication is well presented and structured in four parts. These include an overview including the historical context, legal and ethical issues, mental disorder and offending, and clinical working. It promises to be a most useful tool that can be used to facilitate training and improve our understanding and practices in a most needed area for supporting people with learning disabilities. The book and training resource are user-friendly in format and the way they are written, and follow a well-established series of publications by the Estia Centre.

I am very pleased to welcome this publication on issues in forensic learning disabilities with the excellent contributions by colleagues with knowledge and a wide range of expertise in practice, training and service developments.

It is my hope that this book and training resource will contribute to raising the awareness of all concerned about the needs of people with learning disabilities and forensic issues, and facilitate the necessary reforms.

Nick Bouras, MD, PhD, FRCPsych
Professor Emeritus of Psychiatry
Estia Centre and Maudsley International
Institute of Psychiatry
King's College London

Acknowledgements

Thank you to everyone who has contributed to the handbook and training resource with a special thanks to Dene Robertson for all his extra help and input.

Thank you to Mary Williams and Sarah Halls for their help in proofreading and to the service users at the Eric Shepherd Unit, Hertfordshire Partnership NHS Foundation Trust for their involvement.

Contributors

Jane Barnes is a social worker with 30 years' experience. For much of that time, she has specialised in mental health and learning disabilities. Between 1996 and 2008, she was senior practitioner at the Mental Impairment Evaluation and Treatment Service with the South London and Maudsley Trust. She also spent three years with the Mental Health Act Commission, covering forensic services including Broadmoor. She is a practising approved mental health professional and best interests assessor. She presents to conferences, and lectures on AMHP courses throughout the country.

Christopher Bennett is a consultant clinical psychologist working at the Eric Shepherd Unit, part of Hertfordshire Partnership NHS Foundation Trust. He is a co-facilitator of the sex offender treatment programme run by the unit and works individually with men with learning disabilities who have sexually offended. He provides teaching on forensic issues for people with learning disabilities for two Doctorate in Clinical Psychology training courses. He has also provided training sessions to the probation and police services, on sexual offending in men with learning disabilities.

Nick Bouras is Professor Emeritus of Psychiatry, Estia Centre and Maudsley International, Institute of Psychiatry, King's College London.

Guy Carlile is a founder member and Life President of Medway Swale Advocacy partnerships, a trustee for Action for Advocacy and a former user of mental health and learning disability services. He has lectured at several universities on service user involvement, as part of his campaign to make service users' voices heard. Guy has also worked as the service user co-ordinator at the Estia Centre.

Eddie Chaplin is the principal strategy/research nurse at the Estia Centre, having previously spent over 20 years managing and working within the Mental Impairment Evaluation Service (MIETS) and Behavioural Disorders Services at the Bethlem Royal Hospital. Eddie teaches on a number of academic courses, including the MRCPsych, and devised a forensic module for the MSc Mental Health in Learning Disabilities at the Institute of Psychiatry, along with a 30-credit forensic learning disabilities short course. His current research and clinical interests include self-help for people with learning disabilities, physical restraint and offending behaviour.

Lisa Dakin is the inpatient service manager and lead nurse for Forensic and Prison Services at Oxleas NHS Foundation Trust. She is both RN (LD) and (MH), and has over 20 years' experience of working with offenders with mental health needs or learning disabilities. Lisa has an MSc in Forensic Mental Health and a Postgraduate Certificate in Forensic Psychotherapy.

Quinton Deeley specialises in developmental psychiatry, particularly disorders of social cognition such as autism spectrum disorders and personality disorders associated with challenging behaviours and forensic presentations. In addition to his work as a consultant psychiatrist at the Mental Impairment Evaluation Service (MIETS) and Behavioural Genetics Clinic at the South London and Maudsley NHS Trust, and as consultant psychiatrist at the Springs Unit, Cygnet Hospital Harrow, he is senior lecturer in social behaviour and neurodevelopment at the Institute of Psychiatry, London. There, he undertakes neuroimaging into disorders of social cognition (particularly ASD and criminal psychopathy), and mechanisms underlying dissociative disorders.

Enid Grennan is an occupational therapist currently working in Lewisham Community Team for Adults with Learning Disabilities. She previously worked at the MIETS unit at the Bethlem Royal Hospital where she developed her interest in working with offenders with learning disabilities, and in particular those with autistic spectrum disorder and personality disorder.

Duncan Harding is an academic clinical lecturer in forensic psychiatry, currently working at Broadmoor Hospital and doing research at the Institute of Psychiatry in Declan Murphy's research group.

Sarah Halls is the training officer at the Estia Centre. She graduated in 2002 with a BSc (Hons) in Psychology. Previously, Sarah has worked in outreach, residential and day services for people with learning disabilities and mental health problems. She has also worked as an assistant psychologist, helping to develop and run a specialist assessment and treatment unit for people with learning disabilities and severely challenging behaviour.

Steve Hardy is the training and consultancy manager at the Estia Centre, South London and Maudsley NHS Foundation Trust. He has worked in services for people with learning disabilities for 20 years. He has focused in the area of mental health problems, specifically developing training materials and guidance on best practice for a range of professionals.

Jayne Henry is a clinical psychologist at the Eric Shepherd Unit, a medium secure service for men with learning disabilities. Prior to this, she worked as a clinical psychologist at the MIETS unit at the Bethlem Royal Hospital. Jayne teaches on a number of doctorate courses for clinical psychology and on the MSc Mental Health in Learning Disabilities at the Institute of Psychiatry. Her research and clinical interests include personality disorder, neuropsychology and offending behaviour.

Sujeet Jaydeokar formerly worked as a consultant psychiatrist at the Eric Shepherd Unit, a medium secure unit for people with learning disabilities. He is currently working as a consultant psychiatrist with the Haringey Combined Team – Learning Disabilities. His interests include descriptive psychopathology in people with learning disabilities, autism and human rights legislation.

Max Pickard is a consultant psychiatrist for people with learning disabilities, working for South London and Maudsley NHS Trust, and is a member of the Estia centre. His special interests include neuropsychiatric disorders for people with LD, and offending type behaviours.

Helen Philp qualified as an occupational therapist in 1992, working in a range of psychiatric settings and developing a specialism in learning disabilities, mental health and offending behaviour. She qualified as a systemic family therapist in 2000 and continued working in the same field for a number of years before transferring to child and adolescent mental health services.

Dene Robertson is a consultant psychiatrist and specialises in working with adults with neurodevelopmental disorders and challenging behaviours on the MIETS and Behavioural Disorders Unit at the Maudsley Centre for Behavioural Disorders. His research interests include the determinants of behavioural disorder, developmental disorder and psychosis.

Ailsa Russell is a lecturer in clinical psychology at the Institute of Psychiatry, King's College London. As a chartered psychologist, she works within specialist ASD services in the South London and Maudsley NHS Trust. She is also a part-time academic tutor on the Doctorate in Clinical Psychology training course at the Institute of Psychiatry, King's College London. Current research includes investigating anxiety disorders, particularly obsessive compulsive disorder, in people with ASD, and considering the effectiveness of psychological treatments adapted for this population.

Matthew Stewart is the manager of forensic services for Hertfordshire Partnership Foundation Trust, which encompasses the Eric Shepherd Unit. This provides 36 medium-secure beds for men with learning disabilities, a community forensic service, court diversion services and a prison in-reach team at HMP the Mount. He began his nursing career in the late 1980s, working in one of the old institutions in central Scotland (RSNH). Since 1992, he has worked in a range of forensic services, both in the NHS and independent sectors, which included setting up a learning disability medium secure unit at the North London Forensic Services.

Alex Ward works as an assessment and referrals nurse at the Behavioural Disorders Unit, a national specialist service for adults who have high-functioning autism spectrum disorders and additional mental health difficulties, part of the National and Neurodevelopment Division of the South London and Maudsley NHS Foundation Trust (SLaM). Alex has studied for the MSc in Mental Health Studies and has recently been successful in obtaining a Trustees Committee scholarship to study childhood developmental abnormalities seen in autism spectrum disorders and schizophrenia at the Institute of Psychiatry.

Kiriakos Xenitidis is a consultant psychiatrist at the South London and Maudsley NHS Foundation Trust, working at the Mental Impairment Evaluation and Treatment Service low-secure inpatient unit for adults with learning disabilities, and the Adult Attention Deficit Hyperactivity Disorder (ADHD) Clinic at the Maudsley Hospital. He is an honorary senior lecturer at the Section of Brain Maturation, Institute of Psychiatry.

Evan Yacoub is a consultant psychiatrist for Shoreditch Ward, a new specialist secure inpatient unit for people with learning disabilities at East London Foundation NHS Trust. Previously he worked for both Wandsworth Community Learning Disability Team in the Assessment and Intervention Team and at MIETS Low Secure Unit at the South London and Maudsley NHS Foundation Trust. His interests lie in the assessment and management of patients with learning disabilities and complex needs requiring secure or settings, and in service development to meet the needs of this population.

Donna Yates is a nurse working in Hertfordshire. She has spent much of her career working with service users who can challenge services aggressively, including several years' nursing in forensic units, where she also facilitated anger management and drug and alcohol groups. Donna currently works as a dementia crisis nurse in West Hertfordshire.

Section 1

Background and overview

Section 1
Part A

History, epidemiology and offending

Duncan Harding, Quinton Deeley and Dene Robertson

Introduction

For the purposes of this chapter, we shall take as our definition of learning disabilities an intelligence quotient (IQ) of less than 70, plus associated deficits in adaptive function. The central message of this chapter is that whilst there is some evidence to suggest that there is a relationship between learning disabilities and offending behaviour, it is complex and not fully understood. In an attempt to understand it, we will consider:

- the history of the association between intelligence and crime
- the epidemiology of offending
- characteristics of people with learning disabilities who offend
- theories of offending
- women and offending.

History of association between intelligence and crime

Historically, people with learning disabilities have been considered to have an increased likelihood of committing offences and breaking the law (Goddard, 1912; Clarke, 1894). There were many studies of people with learning disabilities in the prison system in the early 20th century (eg. Woodward (1955), who quotes Sutherland's analysis of more than 300 studies in the USA between 1910 and 1928). However, the literature of the early 20th century has been criticised for hugely exaggerated prevalence figures for 'feeble mindedness' in people who offend (Day, 1993). This is because the intelligence tests used in the criminal population examined mainly verbal abilities, and low scores are likely to have reflected poor educational achievement rather than low intelligence. The professional and public perception that there was a link between learning disabilities and a propensity to offend probably led to the detention of many people with learning disabilities in hospitals and prisons for much longer periods of time than was appropriate or justifiable. For example, in the Baxstrom case in 1966, it was ruled by the US Supreme Court that 967 people had been detained in two hospitals for the 'criminally insane' in New York for longer periods than their maximum sentences allowed (Steadman & Halfon, 1971). This ruling led to their release to civil hospitals and subsequent discharge to the community, when it was noted that very few of the people reoffended and only 21 of the 967 people returned back to a secure hospital environment in the first four years of follow up (Steadman & Halfon, 1971).

More recent reviews of population studies from the early 20th century have shown zero or only modest increases in offending rates in people with learning disabilities compared to control people with normal intelligence (Day, 1993). However, both men and women identified in the Stockholm 1953 birth cohort study as having 'special needs' were three to four times more likely to have committed a crime by the age of 30, compared to people without 'special needs' (Hodgins, 1992). This provided support for the hypothesis that with the closure of long-term psychiatric institutions and the migration of patients with learning disabilities back into the community, there would be a rise in the offending behaviours of that population due to an increase in offending opportunities, and an increase in the identification of 'hidden offences' that would previously have gone on within the walls of the institution (Day, 1993).

In recent years, there has been a shift in attitudes towards people with learning disabilities and/or mental health needs who commit offences and break the law. Examples of this shift include the advent of normalisation (Emerson, 1992), the 'ordinary life' philosophy (King's Fund Centre, 1980; DH, 2001) and the civil rights movement. There is an increased emphasis on trying to understand the needs of a person with learning disabilities who commits an offence. Moreover, it should be noted that over the last 35 years there has been a reduction in the number of offenders with a primary diagnosis of learning disabilities who have been given court disposals to hospital settings in England and elsewhere – for example, 290 in 1973 compared to 91 in 1984 (Lund, 1990; Langton *et al*, 1993). This decrease in the number of court-ordered hospital admissions for such offenders may be due to changes in the nature of psychiatric hospital inpatient resources for the learning disabled, and changes in the focus and philosophy of care. Of particular significance in the UK were the changes to criteria for detention that occurred with the introduction of the Mental Health Act of 1983 (see **Section 2B: Mental Health Act (2007)**).

Epidemiology of offending

Population studies have given some indication of the prevalence of offending behaviour in the learning disabled population. A long-term prospective follow-up study of 411 working class boys living in London and born in 1953 examined the relationship between offending behaviour and IQ (West & Farrington, 1973; Farrington, 1995). Over 30% of this group of boys was convicted of a criminal offence before the age of 32, with a peak conviction rate at 17 years of age. It was found that the boys convicted were more likely to be intellectually impaired, though it was not clearly established how many had IQs below 70. The boys convicted also achieved poor results at school, were smaller, lighter, and had more symptoms of hyperactivity and impulsivity at the age of 10 years. Additionally, they were more likely to have been raised in larger and poorer families, more likely to have parents who were separated or in conflict, to have parents who themselves had been convicted of offences, and in families where harsh or erratic methods of discipline were used. By the age of 32 it was found that half of all the offences were committed by only 6% of the group of boys (Farrington & West, 1993), and that it was possible to predict these 'chronic offenders' from the age of eight to 10 years by certain key factors: 'troublesome' child behaviour; economic deprivation; lower cognitive ability; a convicted parent; and poor child raising (Farrington, 1985). Whilst this study does not specifically examine a learning disabled population, it does illustrate an association between IQ, crime and a range of psychosocial factors.

Other studies have examined people with learning disabilities who are already involved with local services for the learning disabled. In a Cambridge study, 2% of the population of 385 people who had learning disabilities had been potential police suspects in the preceding year for a variety of offences including assault and sexual offences (Lyall *et al*, 1995b). None of the offenders was prosecuted and only one person was formally cautioned. In a study in London, it was found that 9% of people with a learning disability had been police suspects in the previous year (McNulty *et al*, 1995). In this study, most offenders received a caution and about one-third of offenders were formally charged. A much larger study was conducted by McBrien *et al* (2003). Here, adults known to learning disabilities services in a large city were studied, paying attention to both number of convictions and contact with the criminal justice system as suspects. Of the 1,326 adults known to learning disabilities services, it was found that 0.8% were serving a current sentence; 3% had a conviction of some kind; 7% had contact with the criminal justice system as a suspect but were not convicted; and 17% had a challenging behaviour that could have been construed as offending. The study suggests that at some time in their lives, about 10% of people with learning disabilities will have contact with the criminal justice system as suspects. Other studies broadly support these findings (eg.Vaughan *et al*, 2000).

There are many variables that could give rise to bias in such epidemiological studies. For example, the following might *artificially increase* rates of offending behaviour in studies of offending behaviour in people with learning disabilities:

1. Poverty, social deprivation and other factors independently associated with learning disabilities are known to increase the risk of offending behaviour. When such factors are taken into account, the positive correlation between learning disabilities and offending becomes less clear and in a recent study was insignificant (Dickson *et al*, 2005).

2. People with learning disabilities may be less able to evade the police, and may be more vulnerable to arrest. There is some evidence to suggest that offenders with learning disabilities experience an increase in arrest rates for unknown reasons (Robertson, 1988).

Conversely, the following might *artificially decrease* recorded rates of offending behaviour in studies of offending behaviour in people with learning disabilities:

1. People with learning disabilities may not be considered to be responsible for their actions. In some cases, when a person with learning disabilities commits an offence, they will be found to not have the necessary *mens rea* (guilty mind). Therefore, some potential offences do not result in convictions and are not detected in epidemiological studies.

2. A proportion of offending behaviour committed by people with learning disabilities goes unreported for other reasons. For example, in some institutional and care settings, staff are often reluctant to contact the police to report offending behaviour (Lyall *et al*, 1995a).

The epidemiological studies described above have shown that the characteristics of people with a learning disability who offend vary depending on the setting and situation, but on the whole very few people with a severe learning disability are found within the criminal justice system (Lyall *et al*, 1995a; Noble & Conley 1992; Lindsay *et al*, 2002).

Characteristics of people with learning disabilities who offend

Most people with learning disabilities who are convicted for offences are young and male, as observed in offenders of average IQ (Noble & Conley, 1992). There is an over-representation of people with learning disabilities who come from an ethnic minority in courts and prisons, compared to offenders within the normal IQ range (Hayes, 1993; 1996; Noble & Conley, 1992). Certain characteristics of people with learning disabilities who have offended are confirmed in almost all studies. Investigators have often noticed a high incidence of social deprivation and family breakdown and disorder in such offenders (Day, 1988; Winter *et al*, 1997; Barron *et al*, 2004), extended histories of challenging and antisocial behaviours (Day, 1988; Winter *et al*, 1997), increased levels of unemployment (Murphy *et al*, 1995; Barron *et al,* 2004), and an increase in the incidence of abuse in their own personal histories (Lindsay *et al*, 2001; 2004; Barron *et al*, 2004). However, it is not clear if these are more likely in people with learning disabilities compared to those without. A further comparative study of people from a prison population found that, compared to people in the borderline range of IQ, people with learning disabilities were slightly older, less well educated and less likely to be using illicit drugs, and had been brought up in larger families (MacEachron, 1979). Many studies in specialist units and prison settings have demonstrated that there is an increase in the prevalence of mental health needs in those people with learning disabilities who offend (Day, 1988; Murphy *et al*, 1991; Steiner, 1984; White & Wood, 1988; Lindsay *et al*, 2002; 2004; O'Brien, 2002). It remains to be seen whether or not this trend is replicated in offenders with learning disabilities in community settings.

As mentioned above, offending behaviour in people with and without learning disabilities is influenced by a similar set of aetiological factors. These include unstable families, poor parenting, socioeconomic disadvantage, poor educational achievement and substance misuse. However, people with learning disabilities are more likely to experience social disadvantage. Therefore, these factors are likely to contribute significantly more to offending behaviour in this population.

People with learning disabilities do not form one homogeneous group, and there are certain subgroups and conditions linked with learning disabilities that may help us understand the relationship between such disabilities and offending behaviour. Relevant subgroups and/or disorders include:

- autistic spectrum disorders
- hyperkinetic disorder (attention deficit hyperactivity disorder – ADHD)
- brain damage during childhood
- epilepsy
- other mental disorder, including schizophrenia.

In **autistic spectrum disorders**, a prominent characteristic is the reduced ability to empathise with other people. Criminal behaviour, particularly violent criminal behaviour, is inhibited by one's ability to empathise with the victim of the crime, and so a lack of empathy may make a person more likely to commit a violent offence. It is therefore possible to hypothesise a link between autism and violent crime. Asperger's syndrome is an example of a high functioning autistic spectrum disorder, and it has been observed that individuals with this disorder are indeed over-represented in forensic criminal settings (Haskins & Silva, 2006) (see **Section 3B: Neurodevelopmental disorders and offending**).

Hyperkinetic disorder (attention deficit hyperactivity disorder – ADHD) is often associated with behavioural problems and learning disabilities. A significant characteristic of ADHD is poor impulse control, which in itself is a risk factor for offending behaviour. There is also a strong link between childhood ADHD and childhood conduct disorder, which can often lead to adult personality disorder and criminality (Mannuzza *et al*, 1991; Connor *et al*, 2007).

Brain damage during childhood is a possible cause of learning disability, and brain insults can also induce behavioural and personality changes that could precipitate offending behaviour, for example by giving rise to abnormal frontal (executive) or medial temporal lobe function. Such brain damage can be associated with a range of neuropsychological deficits and/or emotional changes, which separately or conjointly predispose to offending, including impaired processing of social-emotional cues, disinhibition, increased irritability, poor impulse control, reduced frustration tolerance and altered sexual drive and regulation (Blair & Cipolotti, 2000).

People with learning disabilities are more likely to develop **epilepsy** than the general population, and epilepsy itself is linked with offending behaviour. This association can occur before or after a seizure, or rarely as a consequence of 'automatic' behaviour during a seizure (Fenwick, 1990).

People with learning disabilities are at increased rates of **other mental disorder, including schizophrenia,** which may predispose to offending. The degree of contribution of such illnesses to offending behaviour in people with learning disabilities is unclear (see **Section 3A: Mental illness, learning disabilities and offending)**.

Finally, a number of social, biological and other factors may interact in order to give rise to altered risk of offending that may be greater than the summed total of the individual factors themselves.

Women and offending

In the general population, men commit more crime than women. Over 90% of all violent offences are committed by men. Female offenders as a group have lower educational achievement and lower than average intelligence scores than women non-offenders. In the Swedish birth cohort study in Stockholm in 1953, the likelihood of a woman with 'special needs' offending was four times greater than a woman with 'average' IQ (Hodgins, 1992). This increase was greater than that observed in the male population. For violent offences, whilst men with learning disabilities had a five times increased risk of offending, the risk for violent offences in the female population was greater by 25 times. However, severe learning disability in women does not seem to be strongly associated with offending behaviour; for example, it was found in a sample of 1,272 randomly selected female offenders awaiting trial that the prevalence of severe learning disabilities in this group was only 0.4% (Teplin *et al*, 1996).

Summary

In summary, there is an association between learning disabilities and offending behaviour, with higher rates of offending in mild learning disability populations and less offending in populations of moderate and severe learning disability. However, research in this area is difficult, and there are many possible confounding factors that confuse results. Whilst learning disability itself may contribute to this increase in risk, social factors associated with learning disabilities are extremely important.

It is important to fully recognise offending behaviour amongst people with learning disabilities in order to properly assess and study the extent of this relationship. Therefore, we need to increase the reporting, detection and conviction rates (where appropriate) for offences committed by people with learning disabilities. This is the only way in which it is possible to make informed decisions about resource allocation. The assessment and treatment of offenders with learning disabilities is an expanding area, and there are prospects for advances in assessment and treatment that offer the hope that offending behaviour in people with learning disabilities can be significantly reduced.

Finally, there have been significant changes in the perception of learning disabled offenders that have occurred alongside broader social shifts in attitude. There does appear to be a growing awareness of the social and other difficulties that people with learning disabilities encounter, and this is reflected by improvements in practice in both the criminal justice system and mental health services, as this book makes clear.

References

Barron P, Hassiotis A & Banes J (2004) Offenders with intellectual disability: a prospective comparative study. *Journal of Intellectual Disability Research* **48** 69-76.

Blair RJR & Cipolotti L (2000) Impaired social response reversal: a case of 'acquired sociopathy'. *Brain* **123** 1122-41.

Clarke (1894) Quoted in: BS Brown and T Courtless (1971) *The Mentally Retarded Offender*. (DHEW Pub. No. (HSM) 72-90-39). Washington, DC: US Government Printing Office.

Connor DF, Ford JD, Albert DB & Doerfler LA (2007) Conduct disorder subtype and comorbidity. *Annals of Clinical Psychiatry* **19** 161-8.

Day K (1988) A hospital-based treatment programme for male mentally handicapped offenders. *British Journal of Psychiatry* **153** 636-44.

Day K (1993) Crime and mental retardation: a review. In: K Howells and CR Hollin (Eds) *Clinical Approaches to the Mentally Disordered Offender* (pp111-43). Chichester: Wiley.

Department of Health (2001) *Valuing People: A new strategy for learning disability for the 21st century*. London: Department of Health.

Dickson K, Emerson E & Hatton C (2005) Self-reported anti-social behaviour: prevalence and risk factors amongst adolescents with and without intellectual disability. *Journal of Intellectual Disability Research* **49** 820-6.

Emerson E (1992) What is normalization? In: H Brown and H Smith (Eds) *Normalisation: A reader for the nineties* (pp1-18). London: Routledge.

Farrington DP (1985) Predicting self-reported and official delinquency. In: DP Farrington and R Taring (Eds) *Prediction in Criminology* (pp150-73). Albany, NY: State University of New York Press.

Farrington DP (1995) The development of offending and antisocial behaviour from childhood: key findings from the Cambridge Study in Delinquent Development. *Journal of Child Psychology and Psychiatry* **360** 929-64.

Farrington DP & West DJ (1993) Criminal, penal and life histories of chronic offenders: risk and protective factors and early identification. *Criminal Behaviour and Mental Health* **3** 492-523.

Fenwick P (1990) Automatism. In: M Bluglass and P Bowden (Eds) *Principles and Practice of Forensic Psychiatry*. London: Churchill Livingstone.

Goddard HH (1912) How shall we educate mental defectives? *The Training School Bulletin* **9** 43.

Haskins BG & Silva JA (2006) Asperger's disorder and criminal behaviour: forensic-psychiatric considerations. *The Journal of the American Academy of Psychiatry and the Law* **34** 374-84.

Hayes S (1993) *People with an Intellectual Disability and the Criminal Justice System: Appearances before the local courts* (Research Report 4). Sydney: New South Wales Reform Commission Report.

Hayes SC (1996) *People with an Intellectual Disability and the Criminal Justice System: Two rural courts*. Research Report Number 5. Sydney: NSW Law Reform Commission.

Hodgins S (1992) Mental disorder, intellectual deficiency, and crime: evidence from a birth cohort. *Archives of General Psychiatry* **6** 476-83.

King's Fund Centre (1980) *An Ordinary Life: Comprehensive locally-based residential services for mentally handicapped people*. London: King's Fund Centre.

Langton J, Crishnan V, Cummella S, Clarke D & Corbett J (1993) Detentions in a mental handicap hospital, a 10 year retrospective study. *Journal of Forensic Psychiatry* **4** 85-95.

Lindsay WR, Law J, Quinn K & Smith AHW (2001) A comparison of physical and sexual abuse histories: sexual and non-sexual offenders with intellectual disability. *Child Abuse and Neglect* **25** 989-95.

Lindsay WR, Murphy L, Smith G *et al* (2004) The dynamic risk assessment and management system: an assessment of immediate risk of violence for individuals with offending and challenging behaviour. *Journal of Applied Research in Intellectual Disabilities* **17** 267-74.

Lindsay WR, Smith AHW, Law J *et al* (2002) A treatment service for sex offenders and abusers with intellectual disability: characteristics of referrals and evaluation. *Journal of Applied Research in Intellectual Disability* **15** 166-74.

Lund J (1990) Mentally retarded criminal offenders in Denmark. *British Journal of Psychiatry* **56** 726-31.

Lyall I, Holland AJ, Collins S & Styles P (1995a) Incidence of persons with a learning disability detained in police custody. A needs assessment for service development. *Medicine, Science and the Law* **35** 61-71.

Lyall I, Holland AJ & Collins S (1995b) Offending by adults with learning disabilities and the attitudes of staff to offending behaviour: implications for service development. *Journal of Intellectual Disability Research* **39** 501-508.

MacEachron AE (1979) Mentally retarded offenders: prevalence and characteristics. *American Journal of Mental Deficiency* **84** 165-76.

Mannuzza S, Klein RG & Addalli KA (1991) Young adult mental status of hyperactive boys and their brothers: a prospective follow-up study. *Journal of the American Academy of Child and Adolescent Psychiatry* **30** 743-51.

McBrien J, Hodgetts A & Gregory J (2003) Offending and risky behaviour in community services for people with intellectual disabilities in one local authority. *Journal of Forensic Psychiatry* **14** 280-97.

McNulty C, Kissi-Deborah R & Newsom-Davies I (1995) Police Involvement with Clients having Intellectual Disabilities: A Pilot Study in South London. *Mental Handicap Research* **8** 129-36.

Murphy G, Harnett H & Holland AJ (1995) A survey of intellectual disabilities amongst men in remand in prison. *Mental Handicap Research* **8** 81-98.

Murphy G, Holland A, Fowler P & Reep J (1991) MIETS: A service option for people with mild mental handicaps and challenging behaviour or psychiatric problems. 1. Philosophy, service and service users. *Mental Handicap Research* **4** 41-66.

Noble JH & Conley RW (1992) Toward an epidemiology of relevant attributes. In: RW Conley, R Luckasson and GN Bouthilet (Eds) *The Criminal Justice System and Mental Retardation* (pp17-53). Baltimore, MD: Paul H Brookes.

O'Brien G (2002) Dual diagnosis in offenders with intellectual disability: setting research priorities – a review of research findings concerning psychiatric disorder (excluding personality disorder) among offenders with intellectual disability. *Journal of Intellectual Disability Research* **46** 21-30.

Robertson G (1988) Arrest patterns among mentally disordered offenders. *British Journal of Psychiatry* **153** 313-6.

Steadman HJ & Halfon A (1971) The Baxstrom patients: Backgrounds and outcomes. *Seminars in Psychiatry* **3** 376-85.

Steiner J (1984) Group counselling with retarded offenders. *Social Work* **29** 181-2.

Teplin LA, Abram KM & McClelland GM (1996) Prevalence of psychiatric disorders among incarcerated women. I. Pretrial jail detainees. *Archives of General Psychiatry* **53** 505-12.

Vaughan PJ, Pullen N & Kelley M (2000) Services for mentally disordered offenders in community psychiatric teams. *Journal of Forensic Psychiatry* **11** 571-86.

West DJ & Farrington DP (1973) *Who Becomes Delinquent?* London: Heinemann.

White DL & Wood H (1988) Lancaster County MRO Programme. In: JA Stark, FJ Menolascino, MH Albarelli & VC Gray (Eds.) *Mental Retardation/Mental Health: Classification, Diagnosis, Treatment, Services*. New York, NY: Springer Verlag.

Winter N, Holland AJ & Collins S (1997) Factors predisposing to suspected offending by adults with self-reported learning disabilities. *Psychological Medicine* **27** 595-607.

Woodward M (1955) The role of low intelligence in delinquency. *British Journal of Delinquency* **5** 281-303.

Section 1
Part B

An introduction to policy and service provision in forensic learning disabilities

Matthew Stewart and Lisa Dakin

Introduction

This chapter examines service provision for offenders with learning disabilities, and the policy and guidance that have influenced the important developments in this area.

Historically, offenders with learning disabilities and those at risk of offending were cared for within institutions such as long-stay hospitals or in high-secure hospitals such as Rampton. More recently, significant changes have taken place in terms of the provision of services for this population as a result of important recommendations from several key reports. The move towards deinstitutionalisation for people with learning disabilities was set out in the 1971 white paper, *Better Services for the Mentally Handicapped* (DHSS, 1971). This outlined the shift in public policy from hospital to community care. The then government's intention to move from institutions to community mental health services was then further developed by the 1975 white paper, *Better Services for the Mentally Ill* (DHSS, 1975).

More specifically, for those who were unable to access generic community services due to their clinical presentation and required secure mental health services, there was *The Glancy Report* (DHSS, 1974) (on 'disturbed and dangerous patients') and *The Butler Report* (Butler Committee, 1975) (on 'mentally disordered offenders'), both of which advocated for the creation of regional secure units in the NHS, later to become known as medium-secure units.

During this period of deinstitutionalisation, although care in the community was the key aspiration, it was also necessary to recognise the needs of mentally disordered offenders and those difficult to manage within community mental health services.

As a result, in 1992 the Reed Review differed from previous guidance in that it took an overview of specific groups of mentally disordered offenders, including people with learning disabilities. *The Reed Report* (Department of Health and Home Office, 1992) was instrumental in recommending new ways of working across agencies. These included least restrictive practice and diversion to local services wherever possible.

Furthermore, in recognition of the anticipated difficulties in providing community services for some adults with learning disabilities, *The Mansell Report* (Mansell, 1993) examined service provision specific to people with learning disabilities and complex needs.

Both *The Reed Report* and *The Mansell Report* contributed to the impetus for the development of locally based secure and non-secure services. These services would be designed to maintain links with the local community and help ease the process of discharge from bed-based to community services. In spite of such guidance, services have developed at different rates across the country. In many areas, the contents of these reports are still an aspiration for the local providers. Due to these variations and inconsistencies in service provision, Mansell updated his report in 2007 (Mansell, 2007) to reflect the current context and challenges.

In 2001, the government published its white paper *Valuing People* (DH, 2001). Since its publication, there has been a steady stream of policies, reports, guidance and legislation regarding the rights of individuals and service provision for people with learning disabilities. This has included: the *Green Light Toolkit* (Foundation for People with Learning Disabilities, 2004), which sets the standards by which mental health provision for this group is judged; the Mental Capacity Act (2005); the Disability Discrimination Act (2005); and the Mental Health Act (2007). Most recently, *Valuing People Now: A new three-year strategy for people with learning disabilities* (DH, 2009) has been released with specific reference to offenders both in custody and in the community.

The development of forensic learning disability services

As highlighted previously, specialist forensic services for people with learning disabilities have developed at varying rates across the country, with some areas still not in a position to provide local services for this population. Growing pressure to remove people and close large institutions was in part due to the perceived negative impact these environments were thought to have on perpetuating, maintaining and increasing the risk of challenging and offending behaviour. However, in some cases this oversimplification resulted in attempts to provide all patients with community placements, regardless of complexity of need and level of risk. This led to both a breakdown in placement and the development of 'mini-institutions' due to the lack of local specialist services and infrastructure. With an absence of and/or difficulty in accessing local services, the consequence has been that people are now placed in out-of-area residential or secure care, hundreds of miles from home. This move towards out-of-area placements presents a number of difficulties for the individuals and their families, which include geographical and cultural isolation, loss of contact with local services, loss of identity, lack of knowledge around care pathways and what is required of them, and individuals being subject to conditions of greater security than is necessary.

In an attempt to address this situation, there have been a number of key policy documents that have focused on the need for local secure pathways and innovative commissioning models, whether NHS or independent sector. The aim of this work has been to overcome the difficulties experienced by this population who commonly fall through the service gaps created by the eligibility criteria of modern mental health services. The *Commissioning Specialist Adult Learning Disability Health Services Good Practice Guidance* (DH, 2007a) brings together good commissioning practice from previous commissioning guidelines (eg. *Establishing Responsible Commissioner: Draft guidance* (DH, 1999a); *The New NHS: Guidance on out of area treatments* (DH, 1999b); and *Commissioning service close to home* (DH, 2004)). It identifies deficits outlined by the Healthcare Commission in recent inquiries, including Cornwall, and Merton and Sutton (Commission for Healthcare Audit and Inspection, 2007a; 2007b). The guidance clearly outlines that commissioners have a responsibility under *The Reed Report* (Department of Health and Home Office, 1992) to ensure:

- services are designed with regard to quality of care and proper attention to individuals' needs
- as far as possible, these should be provided within the community rather than in institutions:
  - under no greater conditions of security than is justified according to danger posed to self and others
  - in a way that promotes rehabilitation and chances of sustaining an independent life as near as possible to home.

Service models

There are currently a number of different forensic learning disability service models. Examples of these include:

- as part of an existing community learning disability team (CLDT)
- as part of existing mental health services
- as part of a specialist mental health team for people with learning disabilities
- as part of a community forensic mental health team
- as part of a specialist stand-alone forensic service with access and interfaces to the appropriate local services, eg:
  - learning disabilities and mental health services
  - criminal justice systems (CJSs) (eg. police, probation, courts and involvement in diversion initiatives)
  - other agencies, such as employment and education to facilitate pathways away from the CJS
  - local learning disabilities partnership boards.

It is recognised that in some areas, implementing recommendations to provide local services is made more difficult due to the small number of people who require forensic services. In these cases, there will be implications in relation to the viability of providing these services in terms of safety, recruitment and finance. This may mean that services need to be provided across districts or regions. The role of, and challenge for, commissioners is to provide a good fit between local, regional and national services.

An overview of forensic learning disability services

Within today's health services, there is a wide range of specialist forensic services that offer care and treatment to people with learning disabilities and forensic needs. These range from inpatient services (which have varying levels of security), specialist community forensic services and prison in-reach teams. As mentioned earlier, there is no uniformity of provision throughout the country. Whether an individual is treated locally or out of area is still very much a postcode lottery; for example, the east of England has medium-secure units for people with learning disabilities, while the south-west of England has no medium-secure beds for this client group.

These regional differences impact on an individual's care pathway. Those who have access to a range of local options can receive treatment from the service most appropriate to their needs, whether that is in a secure bed or supported in the community by specialist teams. Those who receive the necessary care in their local area are more easily able to maintain links with family and other support networks that are likely to improve longer-term outcome.

In those parts of the country with no or few specialist services, it is likely that the care pathway will be haphazard and have the potential to be confused. These areas are often characterised by placements out of area. These moves can also lead to individuals being placed in higher levels of security than is clinically indicated because of a lack of easily accessible and specialist local services for individuals to move on to.

The development of forensic services for people with learning disabilities appears to have been slow and uncoordinated compared with mainstream forensic services. For example, in most regions the NHS provides medium-secure units (MSUs), whereas there are only five such services countrywide for persons with learning disabilities.

A smaller population size means the demand for medium-secure beds for people with learning disabilities will be less than the general population. As a result, it is inevitable that these services may need to cover a wider geographic area to make them viable. With demand greater than the current supply, the independent sector has played a major role in the provision of secure services for offenders with learning disabilities and provides the majority of medium-secure beds for this client group, albeit out of area for the majority. With NHS services being configured regionally, the independent sector is more likely to offer a countrywide service and be more receptive to the current demand.

Current services

In defining care pathways, forensic inpatient services are often categorised by the level of security they offer, whereas community services are more likely to be described in terms of structure and support. The decision regarding the level of security an individual requires at any point in their care pathway, is guided by Standard 5 of the *National Service Framework for Mental Health* (DH, 1999c), which states that an appropriate hospital bed is one that is in the least restrictive environment consistent with the need to protect the service user and the public and is as close to home as possible. Eligibility criteria for admission to a secure bed is set to reflect the level of risk an individual poses as well as the level of security required to contain that risk. Within the forensic care pathway, there are different levels of security. These include:

- high-secure services
- medium-secure services
- low-secure services
- community services.

High-secure services

In England and Wales, high-secure services for people with learning disabilities were historically spread across what were known as the four special hospitals: Rampton; Park Lane and Moss Side (now amalgamated as Ashworth); and Broadmoor. Essentially, high-secure services were for those who presented 'a grave and immediate danger to the public'. In the past 10 years, there has been a push to move more people from high security into conditions of lesser security, according to clinical need and risk. This has led to the National Centre for High Secure Learning Disabilities being established at Rampton Hospital. The aim is to provide a centre of excellence in the care and treatment of offenders with learning disabilities requiring high security, through a critical mass of experts concentrated in a single environment. Due to the relatively small number of patients with learning disabilities in high-secure hospitals (compared to those with mental health needs and personality disorder without learning disabilities), a single service is thought to give greater scope for group treatment through the availability of patients with similar needs or similar offending histories. These benefits are at the expense of services closer to home, where there may not be a large enough demand or structure in place to support such a service.

Medium-secure services

Medium-secure services are provided by the NHS, independent and voluntary sectors. The six providers of medium-secure learning disability services within the NHS vary in terms of whether they provide a national service or serve a core catchment area.

Until recently, what constituted a medium-secure unit had been open to interpretation due to the lack of nationally agreed standards. This led to some anomalies in what is classified as medium or low security, resulting in significant differences in physical and relational security. However, the recent Department of Health publication *Best Practice Guidance: Specification for adult medium-secure services* (DH, 2007b) gives clear standards on what is required to be classified as a medium-secure service and recommends that commissioners use the document as a basis for service agreements. It focuses on seven areas:

1. security – physical, relational and procedural
2. clinical and cost effectiveness
3. governance
4. patient focus
5. accessible and responsive care
6. care environment and amenities
7. public health.

This guidance document is wide-ranging in terms of its coverage but, while some of the standards would be appropriate to learning disability services, others are not.

As part of the development of medium-secure services, it has been noted that the independent sector has shown itself to be adaptable in providing services for those not catered for in certain areas of the NHS, including those with longer-term treatment needs, those with autism spectrum disorder, women's services and those who function in the borderline range of intellectual ability. This may be due to the flexibility enjoyed in developing services outside general NHS constraints, such as location or having to develop on existing sites. Women's services are a particularly important example of this, and here it is generally agreed that there is less of a need for high levels of physical security and more need for greater relational security for the vast majority of this group. However, in comparison to male offenders, the evidence suggests women are more likely to be detained within higher levels of security for much less severe crimes and be detained under civil sections of the Mental Health Act (Bland *et al*, 1999). The majority of women who still require care in a secure environment currently find their needs are met by the independent sector, often due to a lack of NHS provision.

Low-secure services

Low-secure services for people with learning disabilities tend to be much more locally based, serving people from a single county. Local services with their own low-secure units allow patients to benefit from a service that they would otherwise have to move out of area to obtain, possibly to an environment with a higher level of security than required. There are also examples of national low-secure services for more complex referrals (eg. the MIETS Unit in south London).

Low-secure units are an integral part of the care pathway and have additional benefit for people who may be placed out of area in medium-secure environments as the first step in transferring back and reintegration to the local area. Standards for low-secure units are outlined in the *Mental Health Policy Implementation Guide. National Minimum Standards for General Adult Services in Psychiatric Intensive Care Units (PICU) and Low Secure Environments* (DH, 2002).

Community services

Although community forensic services have now become commonplace for offenders with mental health problems, there are as yet few community forensic learning disability services. Where a community service is available, access is dictated by a variety of local models (mentioned earlier) and is usually considered appropriate when the individual is not considered to present a current risk requiring admission, or is a manageable risk within the structure that can be provided by the community service.

Community forensic learning disabilities services are designed to support individuals, to prevent admission and/or relapse, and reduce the risk of recidivism. In addition to the benefits for the individuals concerned, community care also leads to significant cost benefits due to there being less need for expensive bed-based services.

Criminal justice system (CJS)

The primary aim of the criminal justice system (CJS) is to punish and deter offenders. Until recently, it was a commonly held belief that people with a learning disability made up less than 2% of the prison population in the UK. However, a recently commissioned investigation by the Prison Reform Trust, *No One Knows* (Talbot, 2007; 2008), has been able to shed light on the unmet needs of prisoners with learning disabilities. *No One Knows* reported that:

- 7% of prisoners have an IQ of less than 70 and a further 25% have an IQ of less than 80 (Mottram, 2007)

- 23% of juvenile prisoners have an IQ of less than 70 (Harrington *et al*, 2005).

Even allowing for a large margin of error in these figures, they do suggest a need to rethink current working within the CJS, including:

- more joined-up learning disability services within prisons, to provide support
- more learning-disability-specific court diversion schemes to identify people with learning disabilities and to ascertain whether diversion is the most appropriate course of action
- more learning disability prison in-reach teams to provide specialist health services within prisons
- health screening programmes
- links to specialist community teams.

The Bradley Report (Bradley, 2009), an independent review of people with mental health problems and/or learning disabilities within the criminal justice system, goes some way to addressing the issues highlighted above and makes a total of 82 recommendations, which include:

- the establishment of a mentoring programme for people with mental health problems or learning disabilities returning to the community
- the development of a national strategy for rehabilitation services for those leaving prison with mental health problems and/or learning disabilities not subject to supervision from the probation service
- police and courts to have access to liaison and diversion
- the introduction of improved screening to identify people with mental illness and/or learning disabilities at police stations and prison receptions
- the use of community sentences
- criminal justice mental health teams to divert people with serious mental illness and/or learning disabilities.

Conclusions

This chapter has examined and made distinctions between the different types of specialist and secure services available to people with learning disabilities who have forensic needs, and has provided a brief introduction to prison health care, as well as the policy background. It is still the case that much of the care and management of individuals with learning disabilities at risk of offending is delivered by local learning disability services across many parts of the country, and in many cases with little 'specialist' forensic support. For many, this lack of expertise and resources may lead to out-of-area placements, due to the risk and complexity of the individual's presentation and lack of appropriate local services. In spite of a wide range of recent policy initiatives, it is still a 'postcode lottery' with regard to accessing forensic services near to home.

With this in mind it is clear that, in many areas of the country, there is a need for more local services and expertise with interfaces to all areas of the CJS, health and social care.

References

Bland J, Mezey G & Dolan B (1999) Special women, special needs a descriptive study of females in Special Hospitals *The Journal of Forensic Psychiatry* **10** (1) 34-35.

Bradley, Rt Hon The Lord Keith (2009) *Lord Bradley's Review of People with Mental Health Problems or Learning Disabilities in the Criminal Justice System* (*The Bradley Report*). London: Department of Health.

Butler Committee (1975) *Report of the Committee on Mentally Abnormal Offenders* (*The Butler Report*). Cmnd. 6244. London: HMSO.

Commission for Healthcare Audit and Inspection (2007a) *Investigation into the Service for People with Learning Disabilities Provided by Sutton and Merton Primary Care Trust*. London: Commission of Healthcare Audit and Inspection.

Commission for Healthcare Audit and Inspection (2007b) *A Life Like No Other*. London: Commission of Healthcare Audit and Inspection.

Department of Health (1999a) *Establishing Responsible Commissioner: Draft guidance*. HSC Draft. London: Department of Health.

Department of Health (1999b) *The New NHS: Guidance on out of area treatments* (HSC 1999/117). London: Department of Health.

Department of Health (1999c) *National Service Framework for Mental Health: Modern standards and service models*. London: Department of Health.

Department of Health (2001) *Valuing People: A new strategy for learning disability for the 21st Century*. London: Department of Health.

Department of Health (2002) *Mental Health Policy Implementation Guide. National Minimum Standards for General Adult Services in Psychiatric Intensive Care Units (PICU) and Low Secure Environments*. London: Department of Health

Department of Health (2004) *Commissioning Service Close to Home: Note of clarification for commissioners and regulation and inspection authorities*. London: Department of Health.

Department of Health (2007a) *Commissioning Specialist Adult Learning Disability Health Services Good Practice Guidance*. London: Department of Health.

Department of Health (2007b) *Best Practice Guidance: Specification for adult medium-secure services*. London: Department of Health.

Department of Health (2009) *Valuing People Now: A new three-year strategy for people with learning disabilities*. London: Department of Health.

Department of Health and Home Office (1992) *The Reed Report into Mentally Disordered Offenders and Others who Require Similar Services* (CM2088). London: HMSO.

Department of Health and Social Security (1971) *Better Services for the Mentally Handicapped*. Cmnd. 4683. London: HMSO.

Department of Health and Social Security (1974) *Working Party Report on Security in the NHS, Psychiatric Hospitals* (*The Glancy Report*). London: HMSO.

Department of Health and Social Security (1975) *Better Services for the Mentally Ill*. Cmnd. 6233. London: HMSO.

Disability Discrimination Act (2005) Available at: www.opsi.gov.uk/acts/acts2005/ukpga_20050013_en_1.htm (accessed August 2009).

Foundation for People with Learning Disabilities (2004) *Green Light for Mental Health: How good are your mental health services for people with learning disabilities? A service improvement toolkit*. London: Foundation for People with Learning Disabilities.

Harrington RC, Kroll L, Rothwell J, McCarthy K, Bradley D & Bailey S (2005) Psychosocial needs of boys in secure care for serious or persistent offending. *Journal of Child Psychology and Psychiatry* **46** (8) 859-866.

Mansell JL (1993) *Services for People with Learning Disabilities and Challenging Behaviour or Mental Health Needs: Report of a project group*. (*The Mansell Report*). London: Department of Health.

Mansell JL (2007) *Mansell Report 2: Services for people with learning disabilities and challenging behaviour or mental health needs: Report of a project group* (Revised edition). London: Department of Health.

Mental Capacity Act (2005) Available at: www.opsi.gov.uk/acts/acts2005/ukpga_20050009_en_1 (accessed August 2009).

Mental Health Act (2007) Available at: www.opsi.gov.uk/acts/acts2005/20050009.htm (accessed August 2009).

Mottram PG (2007) *HMP Liverpool, Styal and Hindley Study Report*. Liverpool: University of Liverpool.

Talbot J (2007) *No One Knows: Identifying and supporting prisoners with learning difficulties and learning disabilities: the views of prison staff*. London: Prison Reform Trust.

Talbot J (2008) *No One Knows Report and Final Recommendations. Prisoners' Voices: Experiences of the criminal justice system by prisoners with learning disabilities and difficulties*. London: Prison Reform Trust.

Section 1
Part C

Partnerships

Sarah Halls, Steve Hardy and Guy Carlile

Introduction

This chapter examines the growth of service user involvement and the barriers to this. More specifically, it explores service user involvement in both learning disability and mental health services, in particular forensic learning disability services.

The National Health Service (NHS) was established to provide health care for all, free at the point of entry. Since its inception, there has been a paradigm shift from a paternalistic approach towards user-informed and user-friendly services. The NHS Plan (DH, 2000) gave a vision of a new NHS of consumer-based services aimed at ensuring that patients are at the centre of the planning, delivery and evaluation of services, and that moves away from the traditional system of patients being on the outside of care decisions. Other reports, such as *Involving Patients and the Public in Healthcare* (DH, 2001a), also support the implementation of a patient-centred NHS. Patient and public influence and involvement at every level of the service will reinforce the NHS Plan's fundamental aims of providing an NHS that is responsive to the needs of all the different groups across society, regardless of gender, religion, ethnicity, sexuality, age and disability. This has proved to be a challenge and various guidance and policies have been introduced to this end. Such policies include *Involving Patients and the Public in Healthcare* (DH, 2001a) and services such as the Patient Advice and Liaison Service (PALS, DH, 2007).

The public's fundamental right to be consulted regarding health care and user involvement was previously promoted by the World Health Organization in the 1970s. It stated that 'people have a right and a duty to participate individually and collectively in the planning and implementation of their healthcare' (World Health Organization, 1978).

More recently, the development of the Patient Advice and Liaison Service (PALS) (DH, 2007), another vision of the NHS Plan, aimed to enable and empower patients and the public to resolve any issues and use trust services appropriately and effectively. PALS has carried out self-reported user evaluation, which has shown that it has enhanced patients' and service users' experience of accessing and using services within the NHS.

Much research has been undertaken into the benefits of service user involvement within health care, and many agree that the unique information that can be derived from listening to service users and seriously considering their perspective can be valuable when delivering good quality care to the public.

Barriers to service user involvement

With the many reforms in legislation and policy regarding promoting service user involvement, it remains to be seen to what extent it has become reality within mental health services. Policies such as the Mental Health Bill (2006) still tend not to concentrate on the rights of people with mental health problems or on involving people in services, but appear more concerned with the safety of the general public and risk management. Linnett (1999) claims that genuine service user involvement within mental health services is a rare occurrence. He believes the reason for this centres around the fundamental purpose behind service user involvement – to change the balance of power in organisations from professionals to service users themselves – and states that staff are reluctant to relinquish some of their power.

Hickey & Kipping (1998) emphasised that services should consider user involvement as a 'core value', not a 'bolt-on'. Involving people in services takes time, appropriate and continuing levels of funding and commitment from all stakeholders.

Despite services' efforts to encourage user involvement, service users may not be keen to become involved in their care. Service users may be intimidated by involvement in meetings, when they may assume that everyone in attendance is knowledgeable. Meetings are likely to be held in places that service users associate with stigma or where they have had negative experiences (eg. psychiatric hospital).

Staff perceptions and attitudes can be another barrier to user involvement. It is common for staff to be concerned about the consequences of user involvement, with regards to the change in the balance of power. Commitment to user involvement requires staff to move away from the more traditional, prescriptive approaches to care, towards joint working. Approaches and attitudes to care can also be influenced by the personal beliefs of staff, which can be both conscious and unconscious. One example of this is religious beliefs impacting working practice.

Involving people in mental health services

A number of documents have been published by the Department of Health with regards to mental health user involvement. These include *Working in Partnership* (DH, 1994) and *Building Bridges* (DH, 1995), which outline the importance of service user involvement in mental health services as central for future developments within services.

To end the 'postcode lottery of healthcare', the *National Service Framework for Mental Health: Modern standards and service models* (NSF) (DH, 1999) was introduced. One of the fundamental guiding principles was that 'people with mental health problems can expect that services will involve service users and their carers in planning and delivery of care'. It further stated that specific arrangements should be in place to ensure service user and carer involvement. The NSF brought about standards designed to bring equity to service delivery across the country.

Service user involvement in mental health, learning disability and forensic services is beneficial not only to service users themselves, but also to service providers and the government. One of the fundamental benefits of service user involvement is that service users with mental health problems are essentially 'experts' in their own illnesses and their experiences of them, or have the potential to be so. By encouraging service users to be 'experts' in their illness and taking the information they provide into account, it may add to the limited understanding we have of mental health problems. Service users may have a different perspective of their mental health problems and the care they require, which helps to facilitate a more 'patient-centred' service. It is possible that service user involvement for people with mental health problems may in itself serve to be therapeutic to people suffering from mental health problems, in that it may improve confidence and feelings of self-esteem and self-worth, consequently aiding with social inclusion. People with mental health problems are one of the most socially excluded groups within society and encouraging social inclusion is essential for these service users.

Involving people with learning disabilities in services

Historically, people with learning disabilities were placed in long-stay institutions, where service users' involvement was encouraged only to help sustain the institution through activities such as farming and domestic chores; the service users contributed on the institution's terms. Although this may have helped to give the service users a sense of self-respect, it did not give them a say in their care. The era of deinstitutionalisation has seen the closure of institutions over the last few decades with people moving into their local communities.

In 2001, the government published *Valuing People* (DH, 2001c), the first white paper for people with learning disabilities for over 30 years. The aim was not only to promote service user involvement, but also to encourage equality for people with learning disabilities within the wider society, focusing on four key principles: rights, independence, choice and inclusion. Written with help from people with learning disabilities and their families, *Valuing People* puts service users and carers at the centre of the development and delivery of services, stating that: 'people with learning disabilities should be fully involved in the decision-making processes that affect their lives'. It goes on to state that: 'it is no longer acceptable for organisations to view people with learning disabilities as passive recipients of services; they must instead be seen as active partners'.

This was all summarised in *Nothing About Us Without Us* (DH, 2001b), a report produced by the Department of Health in collaboration with the Service Users Advisory Group (the group that helped write *Valuing People*). *Nothing About Us Without Us* is the Service Users Advisory Group's report to the government. *Valuing People Now* (DH, 2009) concentrates on the next steps for the delivery of Valuing People policy. Its emphasis is on ensuring people with learning disabilities have 'real choice and control over the services and support they need and that mainstream public services become more inclusive of people with learning disabilities' (DH, 2009).

Involving people with learning disabilities who have mental health problems in services

The mental health needs of people with learning disabilities is a relatively new concept, and the majority of attention has been given to issues of assessment and treatment. Throughout the 1990s, service user involvement grew steadily in the learning disability field, but those with additional mental health problems were often not included. In reality, many services were battling over who should provide services to this vulnerable group, and it could be argued that involving the individuals themselves was not even a consideration.

With the arrival of *Valuing People* (DH, 2001c), an emphasis was placed on supporting people with learning disabilities and mental health problems into mainstream services, as well as the policy's overall theme of inclusion. This was later supported by the *Green Light Toolkit* (Foundation for People with Learning Disabilities, 2004), an audit tool for local areas to look at how services are meeting mental health needs. The tool was designed to be used by a partnership of stakeholders, with people with learning disabilities at the forefront. The tool includes a set of self-assessments in which user involvement features heavily.

The acknowledgement that those with additional mental health needs have the right to be involved in their care and local services, has seen the development of many initiatives across the UK. One example is The Tuesday Group (Carter *et al*, 2003; Hardy *et al*, 2004). The group was developed from a consultation exercise in south-east London in 2000, in which people with learning disabilities indicated that more emphasis should be placed on mental health promotion. The Tuesday Group was developed soon afterwards, with the aim of promoting the mental health of its members. The group soon evolved, extending its aims and influence. Local universities regularly consult group members on service projects and research and development activities by. In 2003, the group published a report, *Our Mental Health* (Tuesday Group, 2003), outlining their views on what support people need from local services.

Involving people with learning disabilities in forensic services

People with learning disabilities who have offended and been placed in forensic services are a small but vulnerable and significant group. Yet they are (at least in terms of policy and development) one of the remaining groups yet to be fully involved in the inclusion agenda. Only recently, in *Valuing People Now* (DH, 2009), have offenders been specifically mentioned, with the principles of inclusion being applied.

There can be inherent difficulties in working in partnership with people in forensic services. Choice and control are likely to be limited in the context of the care and legal setting. Even with this in mind, involvement should be a priority, with services needing to be realistic and honest with service users about the extent and range of their influence. Individuals should be fully involved in the development of care plans and have a continuing voice on the environment and opportunities in which they reside. As part of an initiative to seek service user opinion, the service user group from a medium-secure unit for people with learning disabilities in Hertfordshire was interviewed (Stewart *et al*, 2009). Six key themes emerged from the results (see **Table 1C.1**), reflecting a wide range of issues relating to the day-to-day lives of the individuals, their immediate environment, their care and treatment and the provision of information.

Table 1C.1: Themed results from service user consultation at a specialist forensic medium-secure unit

Access • Opportunity to have an advocate • Sufficient telephones for everyone to use • Flexible and adequate time for family visits • Shorter period between arrival and gaining community leave	**Choice** • Wide choice about what you eat and drink • Make your own decisions about your bedroom • More choice about things to do
Environment • Individual bedrooms and bathrooms • Windows that you can look through • Large outside area, with regular access • Wide range of leisure opportunities and other activities	**Inclusion** • Full involvement in care plans • Regular meetings between service users and management
Information • An information pack for new service users about the unit, rules, routines etc • Somewhere to get advice if you need it • Information on the Mental Health Act, its different sections and people's rights • More attention paid to consent and medication • Information on medication • Individuals receive copies of their care plans and minutes of meetings	**Personal development** • Opportunities to develop new skills, such as: ❍ anger management ❍ social skills ❍ reading and writing ❍ prevention of offending behaviour ❍ using computers and the internet

Practicalities and principles of promoting service involvement in forensic services

Good practice in involving people with learning disabilities in general is applicable to those who have offended or are at risk of offending, although some of the following may be more pertinent:

- 'It should be remembered that Valuing People applies to all people with learning disabilities. It applies equally to those who have committed or are at risk of committing offences and are in custody or in the community.
- Regardless of the type of service (ie. community; all levels of secure environments), the service's philosophy and culture should embrace and promote involvement, and this should be evident in day-to-day practice.
- All those using forensic services should be fully involved in the development and implementation of their multidisciplinary care plans, regardless of their legal status.

- Environmental and legal restrictions need to be openly discussed with individuals when involving them in care plans, service activities etc. Any plans that are made should be realistic and transparent.

- Information should be made as accessible as possible, especially information that relates to the person's liberty, rights or legal status. They should be supported to understand the information on a regular basis, and it should not be just a one-off event.

- It is common for forensic inpatient services to set up user forums or resident groups. It may be beneficial for such groups to have a shared set of values, clear group rules and boundaries, terms of reference and a clear function.

- Issues or requests raised by individuals or user groups should be acknowledged immediately and the person(s) informed about when they should expect an answer. If the service is unable to solve or meet the request, valid reasons should be given.

- Some individuals may find group situations intimidating. People should be made to feel safe; reinforcing jointly agreed ground rules may support this.

- Other ways of involving individuals may include taking part in induction or ongoing training staff training programmes, interviewing panels, service user representation on planning and development committees and, if part of a larger organisation. representing the service on wider forums etc.

Conclusion

People with learning disabilities who offend, or are at risk of offending, have the right to be as fully involved in their care as any other service user. Although services may need to work within legal and secure restrictions, there are many ways in which they can work in partnership with individuals, empowering them to take control of their lives and work towards a fulfilled life in the community.

References

Carter L, Cronin P, Hobbs T, Mathurine L, Montgomery Y, Peyton L, Smoker J, Stennet B & Zimmock Y (2003) *Our Mental Health. The support people with learning disabilities want for their mental health: A report by the Tuesday Group Lewisham*. London: Estia Centre.

Department of Health (1994) *Working In Partnership*. London: Department of Health.

Department of Health (1995) *Building Bridges: Arrangements for inter-agency working for the care and protection of severely mentally ill people*. London: Department of Health.

Department of Health (1999) *National Service Framework for Mental Health: Modern standards and service models*. London: Department of Health.

Department of Health (2000) *The NHS Plan: A plan for investment, a plan for reform*. London: Department of Health.

Department of Health (2001a) *Involving Patients and the Public in Healthcare: A discussion document*. London: Department of Health.

Department of Health (2001b) *Nothing About Us Without Us*. London: Department of Health.

Department of Health (2001c) *Valuing People: A new strategy for learning disability for the 21st century*. London: Department of Health.

Department of Health (2006) *Mental Health Bill*. London: Department of Health.

Department of Health (2007) *Patient Advice and Liaison Services (PALS) Overview*. London: Department of Health.

Department of Health (2009) *Valuing People Now: A new three-year strategy for people with learning disabilities*. London: Department of Health.

Foundation for People with Learning Disabilities (2004) *Green Light for Mental Health: How good are your mental health services for people with learning disabilities? A service improvement toolkit*. London: Foundation for People with Learning Disabilities.

Hardy S, Essam V & Woodward P (2004) The Tuesday Group: promoting mental health. *Learning Disability Practice* **7** (8) 20-23.

Hickey & Kipping (1998) Exploring the concept of user involvement in mental health through a participation continuum. *Journal of Clinical Nursing* **7** 83-88.

Linnett P (1999) Which way to Utopia? Thoughts on 'user involvement'. *OpenMind* **98** 18-19.

Stewart M, Chaplin E, Henry J & Hardy S (2009) Seeking the opinion of people with learning disabilities and offending behaviour. Presented at OLM-Pavilion conference, London, 24 September.

Tuesday Group (2003) *Our Mental Health: The support people with learning disabilities want for their mental health*. London: Estia Centre. Available at: www.estiacentre.org/workingpapers.html (accessed August 2009).

World Health Organization (1978) *Alma Ata 1978 Primary Health Care*. Geneva: WHO.

Section 2

Legal and ethical

Section 2

Part A

Criminal justice system

Sujeet Jaydeokar and Jane Barnes

Introduction

Professionals working in the field of learning disabilities inevitably come into contact with service users involved with the criminal justice system (CJS). Situations they may find themselves in include:

- emergency assessments in police custody
- Mental Health Act assessments
- meetings with local probation services
- court diversion schemes
- referrals through court, solicitors, prisons, prison in-reach services etc.

The relationship between learning disability and the criminal justice system is a complex one (Baroff *et al*, 2004) and is subject to a number of different interpretations. It raises various questions and points for discussion; for example, can someone with learning disabilities form criminal intent? Should a person with learning disabilities be dealt with through the CJS or through the health care system? Is a person with learning disabilities fit to plead or stand trial? Should someone with learning disabilities go to prison? There is also limited awareness among CJS and health care professionals about these issues and appropriate ways of dealing with them. In many circumstances the outcome will be arbitrary, depending upon the knowledge of the professional involved.

This chapter explores the issues around this population's contact with the CJS, to enable professionals to support people with learning disabilities more appropriately.

Offenders with learning disabilities

Under normal circumstances, a person with learning disabilities should go through the same criminal justice system as anyone else accused of committing a criminal offence. In its simplest form, this usually involves the offender being arrested following a complaint and charged with the alleged offence following investigations. Once the police decide to charge, the crown prosecution service proceeds with prosecution. (This is based on two criteria, which are outlined later in this chapter.) The offender will then appear in a court (crown or magistrate's) and, following trial, will be sentenced if found guilty (for further details see Chapman & Niven, 2000).

However, this process will differ if the defence, prosecution or court, at any stage, decides to raise the issue of learning disabilities. This might result in a person with learning disabilities being diverted from the CJS or dealt with differently within it.

The involvement of a professional working in the field of learning disabilities with the CJS could take any form, eg. as a victim of or witness to an offence carried out by a person with learning disabilities; as an appropriate adult; in an advisory capacity to the police, crown prosecution service, probation services or courts (via written or oral evidence); court diversions; or prison in-reach services. Within these different roles, professionals will face a range of issues and some of these are explored below.

Attitudes and under-reporting

Frequently, there is an attitude amongst carers and practitioners that it is inappropriate to expose people with learning disabilities to the CJS – it is sometimes regarded as an unkind and unhelpful thing to do. Sometimes, police also feel they are not skilled in dealing with these individuals, believing this to be the role of health and social services. They are also aware of the difficulties that can be encountered when trying to involve the CPS, as the label of 'learning disabilities' is often assumed to mean that the witness is unreliable.

Another reason for under-reporting is that care staff often feel it is part of their job to cope with 'challenging behaviour'. If such behaviour is reported, they can be made to feel inadequate or blamed for it (Lyall *et al*, 1995), or may feel that their reputation as a service provider will be tarnished.

However, such attitudes might result in care staff believing that they can expect to be frightened, abused and hurt as part of their job, and that they should not complain when they are. Victims might feel that nobody cares about their experiences, thereby increasing their distress. The alleged perpetrator may feel that their behaviour is acceptable and there are no consequences. This can lead to inappropriate management of underlying issues and risks and may result in a serious crime being committed in the future. Consequences for the victim could also be serious.

Even though the CPS will not take up many of the cases, it is important that offending behaviour is reported to the police. The process of police investigation demonstrates that the situation is being taken seriously and that those behaviours are unacceptable. For the alleged perpetrator, there is the opportunity to refute the allegation or to appreciate the accountability and likely consequences. It also gives an opportunity to manage the situation before it becomes more serious for both perpetrator and victim(s).

Organisations must have clear protocols and procedures, which are understood by both staff and service users, indicating when and how the police should be called. Those procedures need to be owned and applied consistently. Staff must be supported to be robust in requesting police assistance and in co-operating with police investigations.

Evidence and the crown prosecution service

In order for the CPS to decide whether to proceed to prosecution, it has to consider two tests:

- the evidential test (ie. is there sufficient evidence to proceed?)
- the public interest test (ie. would it be in the public interest to proceed?).

It is not the responsibility of staff to conduct an investigation or come to a view about these matters but it is important that they appreciate how to ensure that good evidence is provided and protected. This can be done in a number of ways:

- Clear, detailed notes of the incident should be made as soon as practicable. Instead of using broadly defined terms such as 'challenging behaviour', 'testing boundaries' or 'being hostile or abusive', the notes need to describe precisely what occurred and the manner in which it happened, for example, 'with a raised voice, clenched fist, standing very close'.

- Clearly, medical aid should be provided immediately. However, staff should avoid the temptation to tidy up the crime scene or clean up any victims, as the police may need to establish whether there is forensic evidence that should be protected. If an injury is life threatening or likely to deteriorate, then health care staff have a duty of care to respond to this.

- Staff should be supported to provide victim or witness statements.

The role of the appropriate adult

A police station can be a frightening place and a person with learning disabilities is likely to be more anxious, have comprehension difficulties and be more vulnerable than the general population in such situations. They may also be more suggestible (Clare & Gudjonsson, 1995), thus requiring additional protection from the law. Having someone to support them and advocate for them can make all the difference. A confession by a person with learning disabilities without the presence of an independent person is admitted only after the judge has warned the jury of the special need for caution before basing a conviction on it (Section 77, Police and Criminal Evidence Act (1984)).

If a person with a learning disability is arrested or questioned by the police, the interview must involve an 'appropriate adult' (AA) as defined by the Police and Criminal Evidence Act (1984) Code of Practice C (Home Office, 2004b). In the case of a person who is mentally disordered or mentally vulnerable, this refers to:

- a relative, guardian or other person responsible for his/her care or custody

- someone experienced in dealing with mentally disordered or mentally vulnerable people but who is not a police officer or employed by the police

- failing these, some other responsible adult aged 18 or over who is not a police officer or employed by the police.

A solicitor is unlikely to be an appropriate adult, as required by the code. It is more helpful to have an appropriate adult who is experienced or trained in this field rather than a relative. However, the detainee may express a wish to have a particular person, and this should be respected if practicable. Most social service departments have AA schemes for this purpose. In the interview, the AA will be reminded that s/he is not expected to act simply as an observer. The purpose of the AA is to:

- advise the person being interviewed
- observe whether the interview is being conducted properly and fairly
- facilitate communication with the person being interviewed.

The custody officer should remind the AA and detainee of the right to legal advice. If the AA considers legal advice should be taken, s/he can ask for this to be arranged. If the detainee does not already have a solicitor, the custody officer will call the duty solicitor. The detainee must be given the opportunity to consult a solicitor privately without the AA being present. A solicitor, but not the AA, has legal privilege (ie. can keep confidential anything the detained person says to him/her).

If the person admits to the offence and is able to demonstrate that s/he understands that what s/he did was wrong, the officers may decide to make him/her subject to an official caution for less serious offences. A senior police officer will inform the person that the caution will be put on their records and that, should they be brought before the police again in similar circumstances, s/he may face a court appearance (Chapman & Niven, 2000). This is an important and serious procedure, and can be effective.

Pathways through the criminal justice system

Prior to the trial

If the police decide to charge the person for alleged offences and the CPS decides to proceed with the case, the case will come for trial. A pre-trial period involves decisions on charges, bail, remands etc. The crown court trial commences with the defendant hearing the charge and being asked to plead guilty or not guilty. At this stage, the defence, prosecution or judge can raise the question of the offender's fitness to plead.

The fitness to plead test is a creation of common law (*R v Pritchard* [1836]). Three points are considered:

1. Whether the prisoner is mute of malice (withholding a plea) or not
2. Whether s/he can plead to the indictment (charge) or not
3. Whether s/he is of sufficient intellect to comprehend the course of proceedings on trial:
   - **i.** so as to make a proper defence
   - **ii.** to know that s/he might challenge (any jurors) to whom s/he may object
   - **iii.** to comprehend the details of the evidence.

If there is no certain mode of communicating the details of the trial to the prisoner so that s/he can clearly understand them and be able properly to make his/her defence to the charge, then in legal terms, s/he is 'not of sane mind'. It is not enough that the person may have a general capacity to communicate on ordinary matters. There is no need for the person to have a mental illness or other forms of mental disorder to be classified 'not of sane mind'.

Where a person is not able to understand the trial, it may be entirely appropriate to divert them from the criminal justice process. However, after hearing the medical evidence, if the jury considers that the defendant is not fit to plead, then a trial of the facts takes place to determine whether the defendant committed the act or made the omission charged against him/her (Section 4A(2), (3)). If the jury is not satisfied, they will then acquit the defendant. It is not a full trial, however, and some defences (eg. diminished responsibility) cannot be raised at this stage.

The Criminal Procedure (Insanity) Act (1964) c. 84, as amended by the Criminal Procedure (Insanity and Unfitness to Plead) Act (1991) and the Domestic Violence, Crime and Victims Act (2004), makes provision for persons who are found unfit to be tried, or not guilty by reason of insanity, in respect of criminal charges. The court now has three disposal options:

1. A Section 37 hospital order or guardianship order, Mental Health Act (1983), with or without Section 41 restriction order. (This is retained under the Mental Health Act (2007).)

2. A supervision order

3. Absolute discharge.

(Jones, 2006)

Before the commencement of trial, the person facing the charges could be remanded to custody. The Mental Health Act (1983) c.20 (Part III) as amended by the Mental Health Act (2007) c.12 allows the remand of a person to hospital for either report or treatment at any stage of trial, prior to sentencing. This allows the court to address issues such as the presence of learning disabilities or underlying mental disorder, as defined by the Mental Health Act, fitness to plead etc.

At the trial

At the trial, the issue of learning disabilities could be raised either as an explanation for lack of *mens rea* or as a defence of insanity.

Mens rea could be defined as 'meaning to produce the results or realising that the result is virtually certain or recognising that there is risk of consequences and taking that risk'. However, *mens rea* is not an issue in many cases.

The defence of insanity relies on the principles created by the McNaughten case (*R v McNaughten* [1843]):

1. Every man is presumed to be sane, and to possess a sufficient degree of reason to be responsible for his crime unless the contrary is proved to the jury's satisfaction.

2. To establish a defence on the ground of insanity, it must be clearly proved that:

   - at the time of the committing of the act, the defendant's ability to reason was affected due to disease of mind, resulting in him/her not knowing the nature and quality of the act s/he was doing, or

   - if s/he did know what s/he was doing, s/he did not know it was wrong.

3. Disease of mind need not be a recognised psychiatric disorder.

4. That disease of mind must cause the defendant to have a defect of reason; the defendant's powers of reasoning must have been affected, not simply that they were not used.

If the defendant is found not guilty by reason of insanity (The Criminal Procedure (Insanity) Act (1964)), the judge has a range of options, namely: admission order to a hospital; guardianship order; supervision and treatment order; or absolute discharge.

Where the charge is that of murder, learning disability can be used as a defence for diminished responsibility, if the defendant was 'suffering from such abnormality of mind (arising from a condition of arrested or incomplete development of mind or any inherent causes induced by disease or injury), and that substantially impaired (their) mental responsibility for (their) acts and omissions in doing or being a party to the killing.'

This reduces the conviction from murder to manslaughter, providing a range of disposal options up to and including life imprisonment. For both insanity and diminished responsibility, the defence must prove the defendant to be not of sane mind (burden of proof), whilst the prosecution must prove the defendant guilty based 'on a balance of probabilities' and not 'beyond reasonable doubt' (standard of proof).

Writing a court report

When asked to provide a report to the court, it is essential first to clarify the questions the court wants answers for. This will focus the assessment on those questions. The purpose of a court report is usually to provide a professional assessment of an individual's psychiatric status. It must specifically address clinical issues falling within the parameters of the CJS.

In the case of someone with learning disabilities, the court may also wish to know its consequences for the individual, whether there are any specific aspects amenable to therapy, if so how that therapy might be implemented, and the likely prognosis. While considering the disposal options, it is useful to prepare the list of services the client needs so as to reduce the risks of future offending or manage the risks. It is also helpful to comment on the availability of services in the service user's district. Consideration should also be given to how far those needs could realistically be met within the range of services available locally (Campbell, 1990).

Person with learning disabilities serving a prison sentence

On some occasions, a defendant goes through the entire court proceedings without the question of learning disabilities being raised. At other times, the person with learning disabilities faces a custodial sentence even after this has been raised. Hence it is not uncommon to come across offenders with learning disabilities in prison. The recent *No One Knows* report (Talbot, 2007) found rates in prisons of 7% with IQ below 70; 25% with IQ below 80; and, for young offenders under 18, 23% with IQ below 70.

If there are concerns around their vulnerability in prison, owing to their mental health or underlying mental disorder as defined by the Mental Health Act, then the person could be transferred to a hospital for treatment. After completing the treatment, s/he could be transferred back to the prison to complete the rest of the tariff. If the tariff ends before completion of treatment in the hospital, then the person remains in the hospital for completion of his/her treatment under the provision of the Mental Health Act, until such time that s/he is discharged by the Mental Health Review Tribunal or manager's hearing, or by the responsible clinician (RC) after the completion of treatment (Mental Health Act (2007) c.20 Part III).

Person with learning disabilities as a witness

A person is judged to be a competent and reliable witness if s/he is able:

1. to understand the nature and sanction of the oath
2. to distinguish between fact and fantasy.

Section 16 of the Youth Justice and Criminal Evidence Act (1999) enables certain witnesses (but not the accused) to have the benefit of special measures. These include the witness being screened from the accused or giving evidence by live link, the removal of wigs and gowns while the witness gives evidence, the witness giving evidence in private, video-recording the witness's evidence in chief (use of a prior statement), video-recording cross-examinations and re-examination, examining the witness through an intermediary, and providing aids to communication. A witness may be eligible because of their mental disorder or their significant impairment of intelligence and social functioning.

A mentally disordered person resident in a hospital or attending a medical practitioner for treatment is precluded from serving on a jury (The Juries Act (1974), Section 1(1) (a) and Schedule 1, part 1).

Summary

It is important to deal with the offending behaviour of a person with learning disabilities through the CJS. The CJS has procedures and protocols to deal with these issues appropriately. It is the responsibility of the professionals involved to make sure that the person with learning disabilities is supported appropriately. There is a need for the CJS to have a better understanding of the specific needs of this population. Conversely, there is a need for more awareness of the various processes of the CJS amongst professionals working with service users with learning disabilities. There is also a need for better liaison among the health care professionals and the CJS.

References

Baroff GS, Gunn M & Hayes S (2004) Legal Issues. In: WR Lindsay, JL Taylor and P Sturmey (Eds) *Offenders with Developmental Disabilities*. England: John Wiley & Sons Ltd.

Campbell L (1990) Impairments, disabilities and handicaps: assessment for the court. In: M Bluglass and P Bowden (Eds) *Principles and Practice of Forensic Psychiatry*. London: Churchill Livingston.

Chapman B & Niven S (2000) *A Guide to the Criminal Justice System in England and Wales*. London: Home Office Research, Development and Statistics Directorate.

Clare ICH & Gudjonsson GH (1995) The vulnerability of suspect with intellectual disabilities during police interviews: a review and experimental study of decision-making. *Mental Handicap Research* **8** 110-128.

Home Office (1964) The Criminal Procedure (Insanity) Act (1964), Chapter 84. London: HMSO.

Home Office (1974) The Juries Act (1974), Chapter 23. London: HMSO.

Home Office (1983) The Mental Health Act (1983), Chapter 20, Part III. London: HMSO.

Home Office (1984) Police and Criminal Evidence Act (1984). London: HMSO.

Home Office (1991) The Criminal Procedure (Insanity and Unfitness to Plead) Act (1991). London: HMSO.

Home Office (1999) Youth Justice and Criminal Evidence Act (1999). London: TSO.

Home Office (2004a) The Domestic Violence, Crime and Victims Act (2004). London: TSO.

Home Office (2004b) Code of Practice C for detention, treatment and questioning of persons by police officers. London: TSO.

Home Office (2007) The Mental Health Act, Chapter 12. London: HMSO.

Jones R (2006) *The Mental Health Act Manual* (10th edition). London: Sweet & Maxwell Ltd.

Lyall I, Holland A & Collins S (1995) Offending by adults with learning disabilities: identifying need in one health district. *Mental Handicap Research* **8** 99-109.

R v McNaughten [1843] 8 ER 718; [1843] 10 cl & F 200.

R v Pritchard [1836] 173 ER 135; [1836] 7 Car & P 303.

Talbot J (2007) *No One Knows: Identifying and supporting prisoners with learning difficulties and learning disabilities: the views of prison staff.* London: Prison Reform Trust.

Section 2

Part B

Mental Health Act (2007)

Dene Robertson and Jane Barnes

Introduction

In this chapter, we consider the 2007 Mental Health Act and some of the changes and issues it raises when working with offenders with learning disabilities when they come into contact with mental health services.

The Mental Health Act (1983) as amended by the Mental Health Act (2007)

The Mental Health Act (1983), which has been amended by the Mental Health Act (2007) and came into effect in November 2008, is legislation designed to limit the impact of mental disorder on the affected person and on society. In practice, this means that it is the part of statute law (ie. law that is written down, as opposed to common law, which is based on custom and precedent) that deals with:

a. the circumstances in which it is legitimate to compel a person to accept assessment, treatment or hospital admission for mental disorder
b. safeguards against abuse of process, including access to independent review.

The Mental Health Act (2007) specifies that a number of principles should be taken account of when coming to decisions regarding such matters. These are:

a. respect for (past and present) patients' wishes and feelings
b. minimising restrictions on liberty
c. involvement of patients in planning, developing and delivering care and treatment appropriate to them
d. avoidance of unlawful discrimination
e. the effectiveness of treatment
f. the views of carers and other interested parties
g. respect for diversity generally, including, in particular, diversity of religion, culture and sexual orientation (within the meaning of the Equality Act (2006))
h. patient well-being and safety
i. public safety.

Whilst everyone can agree that these principles are laudable, mental health professionals do not universally agree that the recent Mental Health Act (2007) has been the best way to enshrine them in law.

There are a number of key changes to the Mental Health Act as a result of the 2007 amendments. Many readers will know the terms 'responsible medical officer' (RMO) and 'approved social worker' (ASW). An important change introduced by the Mental Health Act (2007) is a widening of the group of practitioners that can take on the functions previously performed by ASWs and RMOs. In the 2007 Act, the ASW's role has been opened up to a wider group of qualified mental health professionals, and has become that of the 'approved mental health professional (AMHP). The RMO's role has become that of the 'responsible clinician' (RC). An RC can now be a nurse, occupational therapist, psychiatrist, psychologist or social worker. Amongst other roles, AMHPs and RCs (if they are doctors) are involved in making applications and recommendations for detention, and in the provision of reports to the Mental Health Review Tribunals (MHRTs, see page 55). To advocate for service users, independent mental health advocates (IHMAs) are also being introduced. Their function is to help people who have been detained to understand how the Mental Health Act applies to them and what their rights are under the Act, and to support them to exercise those rights. It will be the responsibility of commissioners – primary care trusts or local authorities – to provide IMHAs.

The Mental Health Act (1983) (as amended) is divided into 10 parts. In this chapter, we are mainly concerned with the first five of these.

Part I

Part I of the original 1983 Act has been significantly modified by the Mental Health Act (2007). Now, a mental disorder is defined widely as 'any disorder or disability of mind'. Note that this includes autism spectrum disorders. However, learning disability is *not* a mental disorder within the meaning of the Act unless it is 'associated with seriously irresponsible or abnormally aggressive conduct'. 'Learning disability' is defined as 'a state of arrested or incomplete development of the mind which includes significant impairment of intelligence and social functioning'.

Given the new classification of mental disorder, the treatability test (treatment is likely to 'alleviate or prevent a deterioration' in their condition) has been replaced by a requirement that 'appropriate treatment is available' for the patient concerned. This will apply to all forms of mental disorder. Finally, there is the inclusion of disorders of sexual preference as mental disorder.

Part II

Part II of the Act deals with aspects of compulsory hospital admission, and guardianship. It includes the civil 'sections' most familiar to mental health practitioners in non-forensic settings. With the exception of Section 7 (guardianship orders) and Section 17 (supervised community treatment (SCT) (community treatment orders (CTOs)), these civil sections are not a main focus of this chapter, and detailed information regarding their contents should be sought elsewhere. See **Table 2B.1** for a brief summary.

Table 2B.1: Mental Health Act, Part II	
Section 2 **Assessment order**	Compulsory hospital admission for assessment (or assessment followed by treatment) for up to 28 days for the patient's health, safety, or for the protection of others.
Section 3 **Treatment order**	Compulsory admission to hospital for treatment for up to six months initially. For the patient's health, safety, or for the protection of others.
Section 4 **Emergency assessment order**	Admission for assessment in an emergency for up to 72 hours.
Section 5(2) **Doctor's holding power**	This enables a doctor in charge of a patient's treatment (practically speaking, this may be an on-call ST doctor) to detain a patient in hospital for up to 72 hours whilst s/he is assessed for Section 2 or 3.
Section 5(4) **Nurse's holding power**	This allows a registered nurse to detain a patient for up to six hours when it is not immediately possible to consider the patient under section 5(2) (see above).

Section 7 Guardianship order

Historically, guardianship has been felt to be a very helpful way of supporting people with learning disabilities in the community. The fact that statutory services are required to provide for the patient may ensure better monitoring of the person's care plan. Section 7 of the Mental Health Act (1983) states that a guardianship order should be 'necessary in the interests of the welfare of the patient or for the protection of other person'.

A guardianship order requires that the subject:

a. resides at a place specified by the authority or person named as guardian

b. attends at specified places and times for medical treatment, occupation, education or training (the reader should note that a guardianship order does not require that a patient accepts treatment).

The amendments to the Mental Health Act that came into force in November 2008 brought an additional power to convey the patient to the specified residence.

In addition, access to the patient must be given (at any place where the patient is residing) to any registered medical practitioner, approved social worker or other specified person.

Guardianship can be the outcome of a civil assessment by two doctors and an approved mental health professional (AMHP) under Section 7 but may also be made by a court under the provision of Section 37 (see Part III, page 53-54). The application for a guardianship order must be accepted by the local authority. There must be an identified community responsible clinician (usually a consultant psychiatrist), and an identified care co-ordinator. Guardianship is subject to regular review and can be renewed after six months for a further six months, and at yearly intervals after that. The subject has rights of appeal to the Mental Health Review Tribunal (see page 55).

Section 17 Supervised community treatment (SCT) (community treatment orders (CTOs))

The perception that there was a need to make it possible to compel some patients to accept treatment in the community was a main reason for the review of the Mental Health Act (1983), which has resulted in the 2007 Act. Section 17 of the 1983 Act has been amended and now describes the circumstances in which it is possible to make a community treatment order (CTO). In essence, CTOs 'replace' more limited powers under Section 25A (Aftercare under supervision) of the 1983 Act, which were abolished by the 2007 Act.

A CTO is only an option in circumstances in which:

a. the patient is suffering from a mental disorder of a nature or degree which makes it appropriate for them to receive medical treatment

b. it is necessary for the patient's health or safety, or for the protection of others that the patient should receive such treatment

c. appropriate medical treatment is available.

It must be necessary that the responsible clinician should be able to exercise the power under Section 17E(1) of the Act to recall the patient to hospital.

The CTO must include the conditions with which the patient is required to comply. Two conditions must be included in all cases. These are that patients must make themselves available for medical examination:

a. when needed for consideration of extension of the CTO

b. if necessary, to allow a second opinion approved doctor (SOAD) to provide a (Part 4A) certificate authorising treatment.

Responsible clinicians may also, with the AMHP's agreement, set other conditions that they think are necessary or appropriate to ensure the patient receives medical treatment for mental disorder, prevent harm to the patient's health or safety, and protect other people.

Patients do not have to consent formally to SCT but, in reality, patients will need to be involved in decisions about the treatment to be provided in the community and how and where it is to be given. If they do not agree with the proposed treatment it seems unlikely that they will co-operate with it, even if a piece of paper says they must.

The power to recall is intended to provide a means to respond to evidence of relapse of high-risk behaviour relating to mental disorder before the situation becomes critical and leads to the patient or other people being harmed. The need for recall might arise as a result of relapse, or through a change in the patient's circumstances giving rise to increased risk.

Recall to hospital for treatment should not become a regular or normal event for any patient on SCT. If recall is being used frequently, the responsible clinician should review the patient's treatment plan to consider whether it could be made more acceptable to the patient, or whether in the individual circumstances of the case, the SCT continues to be appropriate.

In order to recall a patient, the responsible clinician must 'serve a notice in writing' on the patient. This may be by first class post to the patient's last known address. If the patient does not respond, s/he can be treated as absent without leave and 'conveyed' to hospital. After recall, the clinical team has a maximum of 72 hours to assess the patient's condition, provide the necessary treatment and determine the next steps. The patient may be well enough to return to the community once treatment has been given, or may need a longer period of assessment or treatment in hospital. After 72 hours, the patient must be released – with the CTO remaining in place.

If the patient requires inpatient treatment for longer than 72 hours after arrival at the hospital, the responsible clinician should consider revoking the CTO. The AMHP must agree. The effect of revoking the CTO is that the patient will again be detained under Section 3 or 37 of the Act, and there is automatic referral to a Mental Health Review Tribunal.

Part III

Part III of the Act focuses on patients concerned in criminal proceedings or under sentence by a court. The following are the sections of Part III likely to be relevant to forensic services.

Section 37 Hospital order

When a person is convicted of an offence punishable with imprisonment, the court may authorise detention in a hospital under Section 37, if it is satisfied (on the written or oral evidence of two registered medical practitioners) that the offender is suffering from a mental disorder (including learning disabilities; see Part I on page 50) of a nature or degree that makes it appropriate for him/her to be detained in a hospital.

Prior to the 2007 Act, the Mental Health Act (1983) required that where the mental disorder was a mental impairment (ie. a learning disability associated with seriously irresponsible or abnormally aggressive conduct), medical treatment was likely to alleviate or prevent deterioration in a patient's condition. This 'treatability test' became a political hot potato because some people thought it was used to exclude some patients from hospital treatment, and that this exposed society to risks that should have been managed by mental health services. After much debate, the 2007 Act replaced the 'treatability' test with an 'appropriate treatment' test. This requires that 'appropriate treatment' should be available for a hospital order to be made. Currently, the definition of 'appropriate treatment' is very wide indeed. Some people argue that this means that psychiatric services are at risk of becoming agents of state control. This matter has aroused strong feelings because it touches on deeply held attachments to differing notions of civil liberty and personal responsibility.

At the time of writing, the effects of the changes introduced in the 2007 Act remain to be seen.

Once a person is made subject to detention under Section 37, s/he ceases to be under the jurisdiction of the court and becomes the responsibility of the treating hospital. The order lasts for six months initially and can be renewed by the responsible clinician for a further six months and then for 12 months at a time. The patient has the right to appeal to the Mental Health Review Tribunal in the second period of detention and each period after that. Discharge can be by either the tribunal or the responsible clinician.

Section 38 Interim hospital order

When a person is convicted before a court of an offence punishable with imprisonment, the court may (before making a hospital order or dealing with him/her in some other way) make an 'interim hospital order' authorising admission to a hospital under Section 38. This is used when the court is satisfied (on the written or oral evidence of two registered medical practitioners) that the offender is suffering from a mental disorder, and that there is reason to suppose that the mental disorder makes a hospital order more appropriate than imprisonment. In this case, at least one of the registered medical practitioners whose evidence was taken into account should be employed at the hospital specified in the order.

An interim hospital order is valid for up to 12 weeks but may be renewed for further periods of not more than 28 days at a time, up to a maximum of 12 months in total. The purpose of this order is to enable an assessment to be made by the hospital on the appropriateness of a hospital order. In essence, the clinical team is coming to a view about whether the person will engage with and benefit from treatment in hospital. During this period, the person continues to be under the jurisdiction of the court. If s/he absconds from hospital s/he may be arrested and returned to court where an alternative disposal will be imposed. At the end of the period, the responsible clinician must inform the court of the recommendation of the team. This could include the view that the person will not benefit from treatment, in which case the court will dispose of the case in some other way. Alternatively, the team could recommend the making of a hospital order under Section 37 with or without a restriction order under Section 41 (see below).

Section 41 Restriction order

Section 41 gives power to higher courts to restrict the discharge of an offender from hospital. When a hospital order is made, it is possible for the court to apply additional 'restriction orders' to the Section if they feel that the offender is at risk of causing further offences and the general public is at risk of 'serious harm'. These special restrictions do not have a time limit, and they require that decisions regarding access to the community (eg. Section 17 Leave) can only be made by the responsible clinician with the permission of the Secretary of State (in reality, those people who work for him or her in the Department of Justice). In practice, the views of the doctors recommending detention under Section 37 are sought on the appropriateness of a restriction order, but the judge can make up his/her mind entirely separately of advice.

A person who is made subject to detention under Sections 37/41 can appeal to the Mental Health Review Tribunal after six months and then yearly, but the tribunal must be chaired by a judge or Queen's Counsel. For this reason, these hearings take longer to arrange. The responsible clinician cannot authorise the discharge of a patient subject to detention under Section 37/41. Discharge can only be authorised by the tribunal or the Ministry of Justice.

Section 47 Transfer direction (with or without Section 49 Restriction direction)

If the Secretary of State is satisfied (by reports from at least two registered medical practitioners) that a person in prison is suffering from a mental disorder of a nature or degree that makes it appropriate for him/her to be detained in a hospital for medical treatment, that person may be moved to and detained in hospital under Section 47 (a 'transfer direction'). Appropriate treatment must be available (see comments about the 'appropriate treatment' test at the foot of page 53). Section 49 (a 'restriction direction') provides for additional restrictions if the Secretary of State thinks that the offender is at risk of causing further offences and that the general public is at risk of serious harm.

When a person is subject to a restriction direction, the responsible clinician must provide reports about the patient (at least annually) to the Secretary of State. These special restrictions do not have a time limit, and they require that decisions about access to the community can only be made with the explicit permission of the Secretary of State via the Ministry of Justice.

The restriction order expires on the earliest date of release from prison. The person can appeal to the MHRT in the second six months after transfer and then yearly. A transferred prisoner who is still subject to a restriction direction and who no longer requires treatment in hospital will be returned to prison if found not to meet criteria for continued detention.

Part IV

This covers the consent to treatment rules. Although these are not dealt with in detail in this chapter, it is worth mentioning changes to Section 58. The new Section 58A states that except for emergencies – where the patient can be treated under Section 62 – electroconvulsive therapy (ECT) cannot be given to a patient with capacity to consent unless they have consented. Where they are not capable of giving consent, the treatment can only be given if this is appropriate and would not conflict with an advance decision that the registered medical practitioner is satisfied is valid or a decision made by an attorney, a deputy or the Court of Protection.

Part V

Mental Health Review Tribunals

Every person who is detained in hospital is entitled to appeal against detention to a Mental Health Review Tribunal (MHRT). An MHRT is made up of three members: a legal member (the president), a medical member (usually a consultant psychiatrist) and a lay member, who is usually from an allied profession such as social work. The MHRT has the status of a civil court and the proceedings will follow rules of evidence, although it will sit in the hospital where the patient is being treated.

MHRTs require written evidence in the form of:

a. a medical report and
b. a social circumstances report.

Oral evidence is given by:

a. the doctor treating the patient (or a representative)
b. somebody who can comment on social circumstances and community facilities (for example, a social worker or community nurse) and
c. a nurse from the ward.

The patient is entitled to free legal representation, which is provided by a solicitor who specialises in mental health law.

The purpose of an MHRT is to ensure that the legal criteria for detention are met and that treatment cannot be provided in any other less restrictive way. It has the power of discharge, can make recommendations, can adjourn for further evidence and can subpoena people to appear.

Managers' hearings

The hospital managers (most commonly senior members of the trust board) have a power to discharge a detained patient (but not a patient on a restriction order). In practice, they delegate this authority. At a managers' hearing, evidence is taken from the treating team and from the patient (who may be represented by a solicitor). Whilst it makes sense for them to make decisions regarding detention based on the criteria for detention, they are not under a legal obligation to do so. Managers' hearings are less formal than MHRTs and can provide a useful learning experience for newly qualified staff with the support of more senior members of staff.

Conditional discharge

In the case of a restricted patient (ie. one detained under Sections 37/41), the MHRT can authorise an absolute discharge, but this is very rare. Much more common is a 'conditional' discharge in which the tribunal directs that the patient comply with clearly specified conditions. These are likely to include the requirement to live in a particular type of accommodation (for example, a staffed group home), to be available to professionals and to follow a care plan or programme. It may also include such things as drug/alcohol screening. Only when the tribunal is satisfied that the conditions are in place will it authorise the conditional discharge of the patient. An MHRT may decide to defer the conditional discharge ('deferred conditional discharge') until such arrangements have been made. Once out in the community, the patient must continue to adhere to those conditions. S/he will be allocated a social supervisor who will be responsible for providing regular reports to the Ministry of Justice about his/her progress in the community. S/he will also have an identified caseworker at the Ministry of Justice who will receive and scrutinise those reports. If the patient does not stick to the conditions or commits a further offence, s/he is liable to be recalled to hospital by the Secretary of State. In that case, the restriction order will be reinstated and s/he will have to start his/her appeal process all over again.

If the person's mental state deteriorates in the community, s/he can be treated in hospital without the conditional discharge being jeopardised. If s/he continues to meet the conditions and progress is good, s/he can apply to the MHRT for an absolute discharge. This usually takes about two years. Once that has been achieved, the person is no longer under the jurisdiction of the legal or health services.

Section 2

Part C

Other legal and ethical considerations

Jane Barnes and Dene Robertson

Introduction

In this chapter, we consider some of the wider legal and ethical issues that relate to working with offenders with learning disabilities by considering relevant policy and legislation. In addition, we will explore some of the ethical issues that may have a direct impact on offenders with learning disabilities and those individuals and teams working with them:

- policy and legislation:
  - protection of vulnerable adults (POVA)
  - Valuing People
  - the care programme approach (CPA)
  - Mental Capacity Act (2005)
  - Deprivation of Liberty Safeguards (DoLS)
- ethical issues.

Relevant policy and legislation

Professionals have a number of tools at their disposal, with which they need to be familiar in order to inform best practice. Below are some of the legislation and policy considerations that are now part of everyday practice for clinicians, and which are designed not only to protect people with learning disabilities but also to consider public safety and state the current Government position. In addition to the Mental Health Act (1983) (as amended by the 2007 Act), care should be delivered within a multiple framework encompassing a number of policy documents:

a. Protection of vulnerable adults (DH, 2009a)
b. Care programme approach (DH, 1995a)
c. Valuing People Now (DH, 2009b)

and legislation such as:

d. Mental Capacity Act (2005)
e. NHS and Community Care Act (1990)
f. Carers Act (1995)
g. The Deprivation of Liberty Safeguards.

These are briefly reviewed below.

(a) Protection of vulnerable adults

Each local authority social services department must have a vulnerable adults policy (other terms, such as 'safeguarding adults', are also in use). This dictates the procedures that should be enacted when a vulnerable adult has been the victim of any form of abuse, offence or neglect. People with learning disabilities are frequently the victims or perpetrators of such incidents and the protection of vulnerable adults (POVA) procedures will be relevant. These procedures do not have the power or weight of legislation and therefore their effectiveness can be variable. In addition, recent enquiries have shown that these procedures may not be well understood by agencies outside the statutory institutions. For example, during its investigation into institutional abuse in homes for people with learning disabilities in Cornwall, the Health Care Commission found that the staff were not familiar with POVA or Valuing People. However, at any time of uncertainty, it is always appropriate to contact the local social services department and ask to speak to the POVA lead.

The Mental Capacity Act (2005) has also introduced a new offence of neglect or abuse of a person who lacks capacity, punishable by up to five years in prison.

(b) The care programme approach

The care programme approach (CPA) was originally developed as part of *Building Bridges: A guide to arrangements for inter-agency working for the care and protection of severely mentally ill people* (DH, 1995a) to tackle, in particular, the needs of people with enduring mental illness who had frequent admissions to hospital (ie. the 'revolving door' patient). It has now been reviewed, however, and is a process and procedure that is used by mental health services to underpin much of their work. Although it has taken some time for the CPA to become incorporated into learning disability service practice, it is essential that those who have been detained under a Mental Health Act treatment order and are covered by Section 117, those with an enduring mental disorder, those requiring multi-agency involvement, and those who present a significant risk to themselves or others, should be on CPA.

CPA has four main elements:

- the assessment of health and social needs
- the formation of a care plan
- a key worker to monitor and co-ordinate care
- regular reviews.

People who do not require CPA are those requiring only minimal support and who do not present a significant risk to themselves or others.

(c) Valuing People Now

Valuing People was initially introduced by the government in 2001 to tackle some of the most common problems experienced by people with learning disability. It concentrates on four main areas: legal and civil rights; independence; choice; and social inclusion. It introduced the concept of person-centred planning. This is not just about keeping the needs of the person at the centre of service provision, but also their wishes and aspirations. *Valuing People Now: A new three-year strategy for people with learning disabilities* (DH, 2009b) outlines the cross-government strategy in light of the vision initially set out in *Valuing People* (DH, 2001): 'that all people with a learning disability are people first with the right to lead their lives like any others, with the same opportunities and responsibilities, and to be treated with the same dignity and respect. They and their families and carers are entitled to the same aspirations and life chances as other citizens' (DH, 2001). The 2009 Valuing People strategy document also includes specific reference to offenders, both in custody and the community.

(d) The Mental Capacity Act (2005)

The Mental Capacity Act (MCA) (2005) puts on statute the common law principles that have governed assessment of capacity for many years. The MCA provides clear guidance about how these principles should be applied by anybody who is providing a service for people who may lack the capacity to make certain decisions.

The MCA is underpinned by five principles:

1. A presumption of capacity: every adult has the right to make his or her own decision and must be assumed to have the capacity to do so unless proved otherwise.

2. Support in decision-making: people must be given all appropriate help before anyone concludes that they cannot make their own decisions.

3. The right to be irrational: individuals who have the capacity to make a particular decision must retain the right to make an eccentric or unwise decision.

4. Best interests: anything done for, or on behalf of, people without capacity must be in their best interests.

5. Least restrictive intervention: anything done for, or on behalf of people who lack capacity should be the least restrictive of their basic rights and freedoms.

An assessment of somebody's capacity is time- and issue-specific and must not be influenced by assumptions relating to label, gender, age or culture. An assessment involves a consideration of whether the person is:

- **a.** able to understand the information relevant to the decision
- **b.** able to retain the information relevant to the decision
- **c.** able to use the information relevant to the decision as part of the process of making the decision

d. able to communicate the decision (whether by talking, using sign language or any other means).

An incapable person would fail at least one of these tests.

In addition, an incapable person would be unable to understand the reasonably foreseeable consequences of:

a. deciding one way or the other, or
b. failing to make the decision.

If it is thought that the person has the capacity to make the decision, he/she is entitled to make whatever decision he/she chooses. This can be difficult for practitioners to accept. If a person does not have the capacity to make the decision, then a view must be taken about what would be in the person's best interests and interventions decided accordingly. This can sometimes mean direct intervention that can also make practitioners uncomfortable.

(e) The NHS and Community Care Act (1990)

The NHS and Community Care Act (1990) provides a duty on social service departments to assess the needs of people living in the community and arrange for the provision of social care services to meet those needs.

(f) The Carers Act (1995)

Under the Carers (Recognition and Services) Act (1995), where a person is deemed to require services under the NHS and Community Care Act (1990), the carer can request the local authority to carry out an assessment of his/her ability to provide and continue to provide care for that person and to take into account the results of that assessment when making a decision about the provision of those services.

(g) Deprivation of Liberty Safeguards (DoLS)

Following the ruling of the European Court of Human Rights in the Bournewood Case (*HL v UK*) in 2004, the government has been under an obligation to develop procedures to ensure that people who lack capacity and are deprived of their liberty have their rights protected. Therefore, the Mental Health Act (2007) introduced Deprivation of Liberty Safeguards (Office of the Public Guardian, 2008) as an amendment to the Mental Capacity Act (2005). These came into force in April 2009, and are based on a best interests assessment.

Ethical issues

Models of care

Health and social services have changed significantly in the way in which they provide care to people with learning disabilities. More recently, this has been influenced by the way services are organised, rather than by the needs of the people concerned. For example, health and social service teams have seen a period of increasing specialisation over the last decade, with eligibility criteria for the provision of services that have become tighter and tighter. This has led to the staff in those teams feeling less and less skilled in any area other than the particular speciality in which they work.

One important consequence of this shift has been the increasingly strict eligibility criteria that must be met in order for an individual to access services. More frequently, a referral to a particular service may be turned down as 'inappropriate', resulting in real people with real needs being pushed from service to service without having their needs met. Inevitably, individuals with more complex needs (eg. mild learning disabilities and comorbid autism, mental illness or personality disorder) fall down the gaps between services. Such people may be vulnerable, chaotic and at times difficult to help. It is not uncommon for this systemic failure to lead to individuals engaging in increasingly risky and dangerous behaviour, which services eventually cannot ignore and which may lead to serious harm to others and incarceration for the individual. This population is often found in forensic services.

Attitudes towards meeting the needs of people with learning disabilities may fall at ends of two extremes, which are described by two opposing models of care (see **Table 2C.1**).

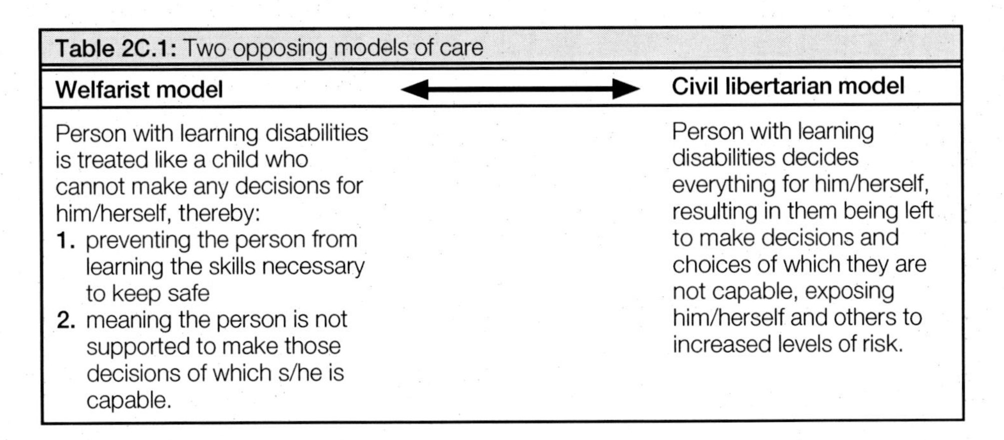

Table 2C.1: Two opposing models of care

Welfarist model	⟷	**Civil libertarian model**
Person with learning disabilities is treated like a child who cannot make any decisions for him/herself, thereby: **1.** preventing the person from learning the skills necessary to keep safe **2.** meaning the person is not supported to make those decisions of which s/he is capable.		Person with learning disabilities decides everything for him/herself, resulting in them being left to make decisions and choices of which they are not capable, exposing him/herself and others to increased levels of risk.

Decisions about when and how services intervene should be based on a thorough assessment of the person's development, cognitive abilities, social circumstances and adaptive skills, but not assumptions based on the label or presentation. This will allow each person to inhabit a unique place on the welfarist/libertarian continuum, and interventions will be at their most effective. It will also ensure that they are enabled to make those decisions of which they are capable, adequately supported with these and protected from making 'decisions' of which they are not capable.

Although some of these assessments are the province of doctors and psychologists, they are not exclusively so. Carers, support workers, day care and residential staff will often know the person best and have crucial information about that person's skills and difficulties. Unfortunately, there are times when this information is lost because other professionals do not ask the questions and the people with the information do not feel confident to offer it.

Confidentiality

Appropriate information sharing is vital if multidisciplinary and inter-agency working is to function effectively. A potential impediment to proper assessment and decision-making is the absence of clarity over how to deal with confidential information. Understanding may be either confused or over-rigid (some professionals seem to share every piece of information without considering confidentiality, whilst others do not think they can share anything). Those working in public services are bound by a duty of confidence, the general principle being that personal information given or received in confidence for one purpose may not be used for a different purpose or passed on to anyone else without consent. However, with proper safeguards, this duty of confidence need not be construed so rigidly that there is a risk of it operating to a person's disadvantage or the disadvantage of the public generally. In essence, information may be passed to someone else on a 'need to know' basis if the following apply:

- where the information is needed because the recipient is or may be involved with the person's care or treatment, or the information is needed for wider reasons (eg. planning/audit)
- the information is required by statute
- passing on the information can be justified for the protection of the public.

Care versus punishment?

People in the caring professions owe their primary duty to those for whom they care. For example, if you are caring for a patient detained under Sections 37/41 of the Mental Health Act (2007), your primary duty to your patient is to alleviate their distress in the least restrictive environment that is consistent with their safety. In some circumstances, this may include protecting them from the consequences of their own actions. However, because care is administered within the social framework that exists within this country, your duty to your patient is limited both by common law and by statute (for example, the Mental Health Act (2007) specifies that you must take into account risk to others, and there is no absolute duty to maintain confidentiality). Thus, our duty to our patient is not absolute: there is an explicit, statutory, and socially determined framework within which we must work.

However, health professionals unavoidably inhabit a number of other roles (these might be national, social, racial etc) at the same time as being carers. In some of these roles, we may perceive that our duty is not primarily to our patient but to one of many other groups to which we belong. Sometimes, these roles and consequent attitudes may act against the best interests of the patient.

For example, as members of wider society we may think that there is a need for a deterrent sentence in all offences of a particular type, even if the offence is directly related to the symptoms of mental illness (for example, arson in the context of a voice saying 'burn it down to save the world'). In such a case, our duty to act in the best interests of our patient conflicts with our duty to make sure that the perpetrator is punished. In forensic care environments, it is imperative that we examine such conflicting motives, otherwise we run the risk of setting ourselves up as judge and jury. A clue that we may be about to act in such a way is that we observe that we are about to do something that is not obviously primarily in the patient's best interest. Sometimes, unexamined attitudes are concealed within apparently medical terminology. For example, it is not unknown for reference to be made to making sure that a patient experiences 'consequences' for a particular behaviour or they 'will not learn'. Such a statement needs to be examined very carefully as it may conceal an abuse of power. To be clear: it is not the responsibility of care staff to meet out punishments (or 'consequences'); there are appropriate statutory agencies for this. Our responsibility to society is discharged when, in addition to treating the patient and performing adequate risk assessment, we contact the police and allow the courts to do their job.

Abuse of power may also arise from a failure to allow the patient to be a fully-fledged member of society. This involves taking responsibility for one's actions. When a patient behaves in a way that would lead any other (non-detained) member of society into conflict with the law, they should be exposed to the same set of social sanctions that would apply to anyone else. For example, because a patient has learning disabilities it does not mean that they should not be reported to the police, charged and prosecuted as would anyone else. In addition, failure to do this may lead to underestimation of risk (both in the institution and wider society) and failure of risk management. Similarly, if a patient with learning disabilities and a mental illness offends (for example, by hitting a nurse) they should be reported to the police. There is a well defined process for establishing whether that person had legal responsibility for their actions, but this is not a decision that should be made by care staff (of whatever grade) prior to appropriate investigation by statutory agencies (including the police). Research suggests that there is significant under-reporting of offending behaviour by adults with learning disabilities by care staff and services (Lyall *et al*, 1995). In order to address this, services need to work to establish a culture where staff feel supported to report offending behaviour to the police. In addition, good links with the local police service need to be established in order to achieve an effective response. Such reporting should be recognised for the role it may play in ensuring that an individual receives the appropriate intervention and support, and also helps inform decisions about the nature of forensic services that should be provided.

Conclusion

Practitioners must be encouraged to think rigorously about how to assess the needs and risks presented by their patients so that interventions can be targeted in the most effective way. There remains a need for greater joined-up thinking and working between services, which will prevent those in need and those presenting risks from falling down the gaps between services. It is not a question of needing more tools; it is a question of using the tools we have effectively. Many of these have been reviewed above. Finally, we should at all times examine our own attitudes in order to avoid prejudice and ensure that we are discharging our primary duty: this is to our patients.

References

Department of Health (1990) NHS and Community Care Act (1990). London: Department of Health.

Department of Health (1995a) *Building Bridges: A guide to arrangements for inter-agency working for the care and protection of severely mentally ill people*. London: HMSO: Components of CPA.

Department of Health (1995b) Carers (Recognition and Services) Act (1995). London: Department of Health.

Department of Health (2001) *Valuing People: A new strategy for learning disability for the 21st Century*. London: Department of Health.

Department of Health (2005) Mental Capacity Act (2005). London: Department of Health

Department of Health (2009a) *Protection of Vulnerable Adults (POVA) scheme in England and Wales for adult placement schemes, domiciliary care agencies and care homes: a practical guide (2009 edition)*. London: Department of Health.

Department of Health (2009b) *Valuing People Now: A new three-year strategy for people with learning disabilities*. London: Department of Health.

HL v UK, European Court of Human Rights, C [2004] J 4269.

Lyall I, Holland A & Collins S (1995) Offending by adults with learning disabilities: identifying need in one health district. *Mental Handicap Research* **8** 99-109.

Office of the Public Guardian (2008) *Deprivation of Liberty Safeguards Code of Practice*. London: TSO.

Section 3

Psychopathology and offending

Section 3
Part A

Mental illness, learning disabilities and offending

Dene Robertson, Jayne Henry, Evan Yacoub
and Eddie Chaplin

Introduction

There has been significant interest in the relationship between mental disorder and offending behaviour for many years, and the 'paranoid schizophrenic' who commits a violent crime is usually front-page news. Often, such treatment by the media appears to turn mental health provision into a political football and increases the stigma to which people with mental disorder are subject. Nevertheless, in the interests of both offender and victim, we must ask ourselves: 'What is the relationship between mental disorder and offending?'. Only in this way can we hope to minimise rates of offending and ensure that offenders are properly managed. In this chapter, we review the relationships, so far as is known, between learning disabilities, other mental disorders and offending behaviour.

The relationship between learning disabilities and mental illness

A number of studies have examined rates of mental illness in people with learning disabilities; these have reported prevalence rates from 20% to 74%. It is now fairly well accepted that people with learning disabilities are more likely to suffer from serious mental illness overall. The wide variation in rates may depend upon the nature of the study (for example, retrospective versus longitudinal) and the study population (for example, community versus institutional, age, IQ, sex etc). In general, most practitioners consider that the lower the IQ, the greater the overall rate of comorbid mental illness.

The identification of comorbid mental illness can be problematic when assessing people with learning disabilities. 'Diagnostic overshadowing', where symptoms of mental or physical disorder are mistakenly attributed to the learning disability itself, can have significant consequences on an individual level, whilst this phenomenon may also contribute to error in estimating rates of mental illness in people with learning disabilities. Clinicians therefore need to be aware of the pitfall of diagnostic overshadowing in order not to falsely attribute the symptoms of mental illness to learning disability in day-to-day practice.

There are other factors that also need to be considered when making a diagnosis. These include:

- **acquiescence:** where the individual is less likely to protest, instead answering in the affirmative; this may help them to cover up their limitations, or seek approval or praise
- **suggestibility:** where the individual is more responsive and receptive to suggestions and is positive towards them
- **psychosocial masking:** limits the expression of psychiatric symptoms in people and is often due to a person's limited life experience. Symptoms the person presents with may appear to be childlike fantasies or have a less complex presentation; for example, a person with a learning disability living in a supported house may believe they are a member of staff as part of their delusions, whereas in the wider general population they may believe they are God or that they rule the world. Expecting a more complex presentation may lead to severe symptoms being missed.

(Turner, 1989)

Cooper *et al* (2007) carried out a population-based study (*n*=1023) using comprehensive individual assessments, and reported a point prevalence of clinically detectable mental ill-health of 40.9%. This figure included problem behaviour and autistic spectrum disorder. When these were excluded, the figure was 22.4%. This particular study is interesting because mental ill-health was associated with excess life events, female gender, lower intellectual ability, smoking, incontinence, not having severe physical disabilities and not having immobility. However, it was not associated with living in a socially deprived area, absence of occupation, communication impairment, epilepsy, hearing impairment or previous institutional residence. Therefore, whilst people with learning disabilities may be disadvantaged in a number of different ways, some types of disadvantage do not appear to be related to increased risk of mental illness. Nevertheless, it is now accepted that the high prevalence of psychiatric disorder in people with learning disabilities is the result of a complicated mixture of neurological, psychological and social factors interacting with each other to increase a person with learning disabilities' vulnerability to mental disorder.

The relationship between mental illness, offending and learning disabilities

It has long been believed that people with mental disorder are at increased risk of offending. There is now a significant amount of evidence to support this for certain disorders. For example, Hodgins *et al* (1996) examined the criminal records of all Danish people born in the four years following 1944 who had been admitted to a psychiatric hospital, and compared them to those never admitted to hospital. **Table 3A.1** shows the 'relative risk' (ie. the number of times more likely a person is) of being convicted of a crime compared to people from the cohort who were never admitted to hospital.

Table 3A.1: Risk of those admitted to psychiatric hospital being convicted of a crime, relative to those never admitted to psychiatric hospital

	Any crime		Violent crime	
Psychiatric disorder	**Male**	**Female**	**Male**	**Female**
Major mental disorder	23.0	9.5	4.48	8.66
Mental retardation	42.4	11.6	7.65	11.81
Organic disorder	31.7	9.6	N/A	N/A
Antisocial personality disorder	32.4	13.6	7.2	12.15
Drug use disorder	46.2	23.7	8.67	15.08
Alcohol use disorder	35.8	18.7	6.68	14.87
Other mental disorder	16.7	7.8	3.15	3.97

(Hodgins *et al*, 1996)

The table demonstrates that people with 'mental retardation', antisocial personality disorder and substance misuse disorders were at highest risk of conviction in this study.

Overall, converging information from the Hodgins *et al* study and a number of other cohort and longitudinal studies suggests that people with mental disorder are more likely to be convicted of an offence than people without. In general, these studies suggest that offending by people with mental disorder is usually 'relatively minor', violence is usually directed towards a family member, and violent offending of the type that reaches the headlines is rare.

One problem with studies of this type is that they often have difficulty in taking into account the possibility of the co-occurrence of learning disabilities and mental illness in the same person (comorbidity or 'dual diagnosis'). This is important because risk of offending may be more closely related to the co-occurrence of mental disorder than any individual mental disorder. This issue of comorbidity is of particular relevance when one considers the relationship between learning disabilities and offending. As discussed in the earlier part of this chapter, people with learning disabilities are more likely to suffer from mental illness. If this is so, it stands to reason that the increased offending rates reported in studies (such as that by Hodgins *et al*, described above) may be due to increased rates of mental illness rather than learning disability itself.

Another way of exploring the relationship between learning disabilities and offending is to ask whether there are greater rates of mental illness in offenders with learning disabilities. There is some evidence to support this hypothesis, and a number of studies suggest that people with learning disabilities who offend are as much as seven times more likely to suffer from mental illness compared to people with learning disabilities who have not offended. For example, Lindsay *et al* (2006b) carried out a 12-year follow up study of patients referred to a community forensic learning disability service in Scotland. The study group included sex offenders, 'other' offenders and female offenders. The rates of mental illness for sex offenders and 'other' offenders were 31.4% and 32.1% respectively. Remarkably, the female offender group had a rate of mental illness of 66.6%, suggesting that female offenders with learning disabilities may be a particularly vulnerable group. These rates for mental illness in the learning disability offending population far exceed corresponding rates in the general population.

Recently, there has been much research interest in the concept of the 'behavioural phenotype' in an attempt to understand how specific genetic abnormalities might be related to patterns of human behaviour. For example, in velocardiofacial syndrome (VCFS), which is due to a microdeletion (missing genetic material) on chromosome 22, there are increased rates of both learning disability and psychosis (these are part of the behavioural phenotype of VCFS). A range of other conditions with behavioural phenotypes exists and many more are likely to be discovered. However, there is as yet no evidence that any behavioural phenotype is associated with learning disabilities, mental illness and offending behaviour. There is likely to be an enormous amount of research interest in this field over the next few decades in both learning disability and non-learning disability populations.

Mental disorder and offending behaviour in people with learning disabilities

Schizophrenia

In general, the presentation of schizophrenia in a person with learning disabilities is likely to be similar to the presentation in a person without learning disabilities. Subtypes are: paranoid, hebephrenic, catatonic, undifferentiated, simple and residual. The International Classification of Diseases (10th Edition) (World Health Organization, 1992; 1993) describes the core features as follows:

> *'These conditions are characterised by fundamental and characteristic distortions of thinking and perception, and by inappropriate or blunted affect. Clear consciousness and intellectual capacity are usually maintained, although certain cognitive deficits may evolve in the course of time. The disturbance involves the most basic functions that give the normal person a feeling of individuality, uniqueness, and self-direction. The most intimate thoughts, feelings and acts are often felt to be known to or shared by others, and explanatory delusions may develop, to the effect that natural or supernatural forces are at work to influence the afflicted individual's thoughts and actions in ways that are often bizarre...*
>
> *'Hallucinations, especially auditory, are common and may comment on the individual's behaviour or thoughts...*
>
> *'Perplexity is also common early on and frequently leads to a belief that everyday situations possess a special, usually sinister, meaning intended uniquely for the individual...*

'Thinking becomes vague, elliptical, and obscure... disturbance of volition may appear as inertia, negativism, or stupor. The onset may be acute, with seriously disturbed behaviour, or insidious, with a gradual development of odd ideas and conduct... In a proportion of cases... the outcome is complete or nearly complete recovery.'

Delusions and hallucinations, referred to in the description above, are sometimes known as 'positive' symptoms of schizophrenia. A delusion is a fixed, false belief, held in the face of evidence to the contrary, that is out of keeping with the patient's sociocultural milieu; a hallucination is a perception in the absence of a stimulus.

Making a diagnosis early in the course of a schizophrenic illness may be difficult, whether or not there is learning disability. This is because positive symptoms of schizophrenia may not be obviously present, and non-specific signs of behavioural abnormality may be the only presenting features (for example, school refusal, truanting, failure of occupation, disorganised behaviour or delinquency). Diagnostic overshadowing is an obvious possibility, here. As the disease evolves, the characteristic positive symptoms may become more prominent and enable reliable diagnosis. Moreover, transient psychotic states are recognised to be common in the non-learning disability population and have been reported to occur with increased frequency in people with learning disabilities (Sovner, 1986). In the acute episode, such states may be indistinguishable from schizophrenia. Therefore, the diagnosis of schizophrenia should be made with caution unless there is clear history of characteristic features over an extended period of time.

In Turner's (1989) review of schizophrenia and learning disability, prevalence data ranging between 1.3% and 3.7% were reported. This compares with an estimated prevalence in the general population of roughly 0.5%, suggesting that schizophrenia is at least twice, and possibly as much as seven times, more common in the learning disability population. However, establishing a diagnosis of schizophrenia in a person with learning disabilities may be more difficult than in a person without. One reason is that people with learning disabilities may have increased difficulty reporting their thought contents. In the absence of such reports, it may be extremely difficult to establish the presence of the positive symptoms that are necessary for making the diagnosis. On the other hand, delusions of reference have been reported to be more common in people with learning disabilities. It is interesting to speculate that one reason may be that, as a result of learning disabilities, a person may have difficulty in mounting a logical challenge to abnormal thought contents, and that the 'threshold' for achieving delusional intensity may therefore be lower.

Associations between different types of positive psychotic symptoms and offending have been explored in the non-learning disability population. For example, nearly all types of delusional ideas are reported in one study or another to have been associated with a particular risk of violence. However, these studies have infrequently been replicated, and it is important to remember that the vast majority of patients with delusional ideas do not act on them. Similarly, it is commonly believed that command auditory hallucinations (ie. those that contain instructions to behave in a particular way) are an indicator of risk, though consistent evidence for a simple relationship is lacking. Indeed, in one study, patients with command hallucinations were found to be no more violent than matched controls (Zisook *et al*, 1995).

Interest has recently been expressed in 'threat/control override' (TCO) symptoms as a potential mechanism whereby psychotic symptoms might give rise to offending. TCO symptoms are those in which a sufferer believes that others wish to do them harm (threat), and in which they are unable to control their own thinking as a result of forces outside their own control or believe that thoughts have been put into their heads (control override). Some evidence for a link between TCO symptoms and offending has been demonstrated (Link *et al*, 1998), although this remains an active area of research.

Smith *et al* (2008) reported that learning disability offenders with schizophrenia were more likely than learning disability offenders with mood disorders to commit a violent offence. Once treated, learning disability offenders with schizophrenia had a lower reoffending rate compared to those without schizophrenia. This study suggests that treatment for schizophrenia may ameliorate but not completely abolish the associated risk of offending.

It should be noted that the negative symptoms of schizophrenia, which include lack of motivation, social withdrawal and poverty of thought, are not known to act as protective factors against the risk of offending behaviour. (Note that it is a common misperception that the term 'negative symptoms' refers to the absence of positive symptoms in a person with schizophrenia.) From the clinical point of view, negative symptoms are at least as much of a challenge to rehabilitative efforts as positive symptoms because they are significantly less likely to respond to antipsychotic medication.

Mood disorder

This term includes a number of different diagnoses, of which the most important are bipolar affective disorder, depressive disorder and persistent mood disorders.

- In bipolar affective disorder (also known as manic depressive psychosis), episodes of both depressive disorder and mania have occurred. Patients may or may not experience psychotic symptoms.

- Depressive disorder may be of mild, moderate or severe intensity, and may or may not be associated with 'biological' symptoms (including disturbance of sleep, appetite, libido and concentration). There may be slowing of thought and motor activity ('psychomotor retardation'). If the disorder is severe it may be associated with mood congruent psychotic symptoms including delusions (often of guilt or worthlessness) and hallucinations with mood congruent content. Depressive disorder is very common and is often recurrent.

- Persistent mood disorders: in cyclothymia, there is a persistent instability of mood involving numerous periods of mild depression and mild elation of insufficient intensity to meet criteria for a diagnosis of bipolar disorder. In dysthymia, there is chronic lowering of mood insufficient to meet criteria for a diagnosis of depressive disorder.

Some studies suggest that depressive reactions to adverse life events are more common in the learning disability population (rates of up to 33% have been reported). Rather surprisingly (given this finding and knowledge of the social stressors to which people with learning disabilities may be subject), the prevalence of mood disorders overall (including bipolar disorder) does not appear to be significantly greater in people with learning disabilities. Most studies report rates of 1.2% to 1.9%, and these do not differ significantly from rates in the general population. It is important to remember, however, that some people with learning disabilities may have difficulty identifying their own mood states (alexithymia), and most will have more difficulty than non-learning disabled people in reporting their mood states to mental health workers. As a result, it is often necessary to infer a patient's mood state from their appearance and behaviour, or from episodic variations in behaviour. For example, a depressed patient with learning disabilities may show periods of decreased interest in daytime activities together with poor sleep, irritability and weight loss but be unable to describe unhappiness or sadness. Recognising depressive disorder in this way may be labour intensive, but is important because depressive disorder is amenable to treatment. In the general adult forensic psychiatric literature, there are reported associations between depressive disorder and shoplifting. This issue remains contentious, and there is no corresponding forensic learning disability literature. Depressive disorder is often associated with irritability in both learning disability and non-learning disability populations, and this may lead to aggressive behaviour, although there is no evidence that depressive disorder leads to increased risk of violent offending in people with learning disabilities.

Manic patients may behave in a grandiose, irritable or disinhibited way, and this may lead to public order offences and violent offending. It has been reported that people with learning disabilities and hypomania who committed assault were less likely to reoffend than learning disability offenders with no mental illness (Smith *et al*, 2008). One interpretation is that the illness confers risk for the offence, and that treatment of the illness decreases risk of offending. Whilst violent offences obviously occur in the context of mania/hypomania, more commonly patients fail to pay their bills and spend money they do not have, thus committing fraud, and incur considerable debt.

People with learning disabilities are reported to suffer from increased rates of more minor degrees of mood abnormality (especially increased depressive symptoms), although there is no established relationship between persistent mood disorders and offending behaviour in people with learning disabilities.

Anxiety disorder

Anxiety disorders in people with learning disabilities have only recently received significant attention. However, it is now understood that anxiety disorders and other disorders that would formerly have been labelled 'neurotic' are at least as common in the learning disability as in the non-learning disability population. Note that anxiety and attention deficit disorders are far more common in people with pervasive developmental disorders (these disorders are dealt with in **Section 3B: Neurodevelopmental disorders and offending**).

Personality disorder

The Office for National Statistics (ONS) survey *Psychiatric Morbidity among Adults Living in Private Households, 2000* (Singleton *et al*, 2001) reported prevalence rates of personality disorders of 5.4% for men and 3.4% for women in the general population. The prevalence of personality disorder increases substantially in a psychiatric population, varying between 36% and 67% (NIMHE, 2003a), and increases further in the forensic population, where it ranges from 41% in high-secure hospitals to 78% in prisons (Singleton *et al*, 1998; Taylor *et al*, 1998). Following the publication of DSM-III (American Psychiatric Association, 1980) there was a significant increase in research on personality disorder, which has contributed to important policy guidance such as *Personality Disorder: No Longer a Diagnosis of Exclusion* (NIMHE, 2003b) and *Personality Disorder Capabilities Framework: Breaking the Cycle of Rejection* (NIMHE, 2003a).

Despite the growing knowledge base relating to adults with personality disorder in mainstream and forensic populations, similar research interest in learning disability populations has been sporadic. A recent review by Alexander and Cooray (2003) found huge variation in the prevalence of personality disorder in a learning disability population ranging from 1% to 91% in the community and 22% to 92% in hospital settings. They suggest this huge range is too large to be explained by real differences and conclude the diagnosis of personality disorder in this population is complex and difficult. More recently, Lindsay *et al* (2006a) have been investigating both inpatient and community forensic learning disability populations. They found a higher prevalence of personality disorder in a high-secure setting (56%) and no significant difference between medium/low secure (26.2%) and community (33.3%) settings. As in mainstream forensic populations, the most common diagnosis in all three settings was antisocial personality disorder. Alexander *et al* (2006) explored the long-term outcome of patients discharged from medium security for offenders with learning disabilities. They found that, within the 12-year follow-up period, patients with personality disorder were nine times more likely to reoffend.

Despite growing interest in the prevalence of personality disorder in the learning disability population and the possible associated risk in terms of offending behaviour, as yet, there has been minimal research focusing on the diagnostic process. Diagnosis of personality disorder for people with learning disabilities continues to be seen by some as controversial, due to developmental and behavioural issues associated with learning disabilities that have implications for diagnosis. For example, emotional immaturity or impaired theory of mind (as are found in specific developmental disorders such as autism) are associated with some characteristics of personality disorders such as the inability to empathise (Morrissey *et al*, 2005). In addition, many people with learning disabilities will have experienced long-term institutional care and problems integrating into society. For many, this has posed problems in a number of areas, including employment, leisure, forming friendships and relationships, and being comfortable socially.

Gathering information from a range of sources such as self-report and informant ratings, using a variety of methods including interview, psychometric tools and observation, is important when assessing people with complex needs. The challenges facing clinicians involved in the diagnostic process are further exacerbated when working with service users who have a forensic history. However, the identification of personality disorder is particularly important in forensic populations due to the consistent link between antisocial personality disorder and violent offending (Morrissey *et al*, 2007).There is also general agreement that it can contribute to poor outcome and recidivism (Grettan *et al*, 2001). As such, the identification of personality disorder is essential, not only in terms of delivering the appropriate treatment package but also to ensure that adequate risk assessment and management strategies are in place.

At present, it is unclear whether personality disorder assessment measures constructed and validated on offenders without a learning disability are valid or reliable with a learning disability population, and therefore we cannot be certain of their usefulness. Currently, there are a small number of studies validating the Standardised Assessment of Personality (SAP) (Mann *et al,* 1981) and the Psychopathy Checklist Revised (PCL-R) (Hare, 1991) for people with learning disabilities. Reid & Ballinger (1987) investigated the use of the SAP in 100 inpatient adults with mild to moderate learning disabilities and concluded the SAP was a useful, reliable and relevant tool that could be used without modification in this population. However, they did note that it did not take into account the difficulty in applying diagnostic criteria to adults with learning disabilities. Flynn *et al* (2002) found support for the validity of the SAP in this population but suggested it was difficult for informants to make confident inferences about complex cognitive constructs, and results were not always congruent with clinical diagnosis.

Substance misuse

Growing interest in the use of alcohol and illicit drugs by adults with learning disabilities has led to a slow but steady increase in the literature examining this important issue. Taggart *et al* (2008) summarised this literature and highlighted the following findings:

- Although much of the literature points to a lower prevalence of 'use' and 'misuse' of substances by adults with learning disabilities, it is possible that the figures available are underestimates.

- There is some evidence (McGillicuddy, 2006) that, although they have lower rates of alcohol use, people with learning disabilities who do use alcohol appear to be at increased risk of going on to misuse alcohol and illicit drugs.

- There are a number of factors associated primarily with learning disabilities that might contribute to an increased risk of substance misuse. These include: compromised tolerance to drugs; the co-existence of a mental health problem; low self-esteem; disempowerment; impulsivity; cognitive limitations; unemployment; social isolation; and desire for social acceptance.

- Emerging research suggests a link between substance misuse and offending behaviour in people with learning disabilities (Klimecki *et al*, 1994 and Huxley *et al*, 2007).

- Community learning disability teams (CLDTs) and community drug and alcohol teams (CDATs) have difficulty meeting the needs of this population. A variety of models have been put in place around the country to try and bridge the gap between the two specialisms, such as nurses from both CLDTs and CDATs working jointly, or individual professionals within either a CLDT or a CDAT developing a special interest and providing a service within their teams.

In view of these findings, the inclusion of substance misuse as part of the assessment process is not only essential in order to adequately explore presenting mental health problems, but also to consider the related risk factors in terms of offending behaviour and physical health problems. As with offending in mainstream forensic populations, it is not uncommon to find acquisitive offences being carried out to fund substance misuse. Including an assessment of previous and current substance misuse is essential in developing a formulation regarding offending behaviour.

However, in terms of examining the association between mental disorder and substance misuse in offenders with learning disabilities, there is as yet no literature available to inform best practice in terms of assessment and treatment. Over the past five years, there has been a great deal of interest in the role of substance misuse – particularly cannabis and the stronger variation of 'skunk' – in the development of psychosis. A distinction has been made between drug-induced psychosis, where symptoms are present while the person is under the influence of illicit substances, and comorbid mental illness, where psychosis may be due to an underlying illness such as schizophrenia. Furthermore, there is now growing evidence that adolescent cannabis use increases the risk of psychosis (Arseneault *et al*, 2002). A comprehensive psychiatric assessment will be necessary in order to establish the presence of drug-induced or comorbid mental illness, in order that the appropriate treatment options can be explored. Although the available research does not as yet refer specifically to adults with learning disabilities, there is no reason to assume that the risks in relation to substance misuse and mental disorder are any less. Where possible, collaboration with CDATs may provide joint working between specialisms, which is likely to benefit the service user.

Drug treatment

In general, there is little evidence that pharmacological treatments of mental illness in people with learning disabilities differ from those without. However, people with learning disabilities may be more liable to suffer from the side effects of some drugs even at low dose, and a cautious approach to dose increase, particularly of antipsychotic medication, is often appropriate.

This chapter has addressed the difficulty that some people with learning disabilities may have in reporting on their thought contents and mood state. In such cases, additional weight often has to be placed on the assessment of behaviour in order to make a diagnosis. The same is often true of assessing response to treatment. For example, if it is hypothesised that a patient is suffering from a depressive disorder for which the pharmacological treatment is an antidepressant, it may be appropriate to make quantitative observations of a patient's behaviour pre- and post-medication in order to establish whether and to what degree they respond. Such measurements might include sleep charts, weight charts, rates of attendance at occupational activities, time spent in their room, interest in playing pool, and many others. The chosen measure in such a case will often reflect what is known of the interests and behaviour patterns of the patient prior to the onset of the presumed illness, as the idea is to capture change in behaviour over time. If a number of interventions are made over a period of time in order to establish the most effective of a series of potential treatments, this is sometimes known as a sequential hypothesis testing approach. Such an approach is to be encouraged, as:

a. it is most likely to lead to the continued prescription of the most appropriate treatment regimen
b. it is least likely to expose the patient to the long-term side effects of unhelpful medication.

National Institute of Clinical Excellence (NICE) guidelines for the treatment of schizophrenia now stipulate that clozapine (an atypical antipsychotic drug) should be made available to patients whose illness has proven resistant to two different antipsychotic drugs. Clinical experience suggests that patients with learning disabilities may have greater difficulty accessing clozapine, and may therefore be more likely to suffer from the continued distress associated with the symptoms of schizophrenia. Similarly, people with learning disabilities who have treatment-resistant mood disorders are rarely treated with electroconvulsive therapy (ECT), and it is possible that this population is being deprived of an effective treatment for severe psychiatric distress. Difficulties in making such treatments available for patients is in some cases likely to be related to service configuration, but it appears sometimes to be due to a lack of assertive advocacy. It is the responsibility of those of us who work with people with learning disabilities to make sure that we provide for our patients a quality of service at least as high as that provided by our colleagues for people without learning disabilities.

Finally, recent studies have explored the use of antipsychotic medication for people with learning disabilities and challenging behaviour. Research suggests that between 22% and 45% of adults with learning disabilities in hospital and up 20% living in the community are prescribed antipsychotic medication (Branford, 1994). This suggests that a significant proportion may be prescribed antipsychotic medication for the management of challenging behaviour where there is no associated psychiatric disorder (Tyrer *et al,* 2008). In a recent study (Tyrer *et al*, 2008), one group of patients was given haloperidol, a second group risperidone and a third group a placebo. Aggression decreased substantially with all three treatments by four weeks into the trial, but patients receiving the placebo improved most. Overall, this study suggests that the routine prescription of antipsychotic drugs early in the management of aggressive challenging behaviour, even in low doses, should no longer be regarded as a satisfactory form of care.

Psychological treatment

Over the past 10 years, there have been significant developments in the psychological treatment of adults with learning disabilities who have mental health problems. Traditionally, psychological services within CLDTs have focused primarily on providing well-established evidence-based approaches for challenging behaviour. However, the growing literature exploring the efficacy of psychological therapies for disorders such as depression, anxiety, trauma and, more recently, psychosis (Lindsay *et al*, 1993; 1997; Hollins & Sinason 2000; Oathamshaw & Haddock 2006; Barrowcliff, 2007) has begun to challenge the idea that adults with learning disabilities are not able to benefit from individual or group psychotherapy. This shift was in part supported by the evidence indicating that people with learning disabilities are able to self-report on their emotional states, in addition to the recognition that this population should have access to therapeutic interventions that are not only available to, but have been found to be efficacious for, the general population (Lindsay *et al*, 1994, Whitehouse *et al*, 2006).

Promising results from case studies and case series, in addition to meta-analysis review (Prout & Nowak-Drabik, 2003) have meant that although the evidence base regarding the efficacy of psychotherapeutic interventions is still limited, there is growing support for the use of cognitive behavioural therapy for people with learning disabilities. As a result of this, recent government developments such as *The National Service Framework for Mental Health: Modern standards and service models* (DH, 1999), which has led to the provision of the Improving Access to Psychological Therapies (IAPT) programme, should, in theory, be available for adults with learning disabilities.

Despite these promising developments, people with learning disabilities and complex needs, which may include severe and enduring mental illness and offending behaviour, are currently less likely to access the new initiatives. This population will require specialist psychological services from both in-community and inpatient settings. Unfortunately, as discussed in previous sections, it is not uncommon for offenders with learning disabilities – particularly those who function in the borderline range of intellectual ability – to fall between the gaps of these services based on a range of service criteria. Furthermore, it can be difficult to access therapists with the specialist skills required for working with this population.

Conclusion

In examining the link between mental disorder and offending, reported prevalence rates can vary enormously between studies. In spite of this, there is general agreement that people with learning disabilities are more likely overall to suffer from severe mental illness. This is the result of a complicated mixture of neurological, psychological and social factors interacting with each other to increase vulnerability to mental disorder. In establishing a diagnosis, problems in reporting symptoms can often be overcome by using behavioural and observational techniques with the person.

It has been established that people with certain mental disorders such as personality disorder or comorbid issues such as substance misuse may suffer from higher rates of criminality; however, the evidence from longitudinal studies suggests they are more likely to be convicted, albeit for relatively minor offences. The issue regarding learning disabilities is whether this increase is due to the increased rates of mental disorder in this population or the learning disability itself. Another consideration is substance abuse. The growing interest in substance abuse in people with learning disabilities has pointed to a lower prevalence, although emerging research does suggest a link between substance abuse and offending in people with learning disabilities.

Finally, with regard to treatment, the last 10 years have seen significant developments in psychological treatments, with promising results being reported; the use of cognitive behavioural techniques has also increased.

As research in the field of forensic learning disability develops, so too does the understanding of what constitutes best practice. New research and information across a number of themes (epidemiology, substance abuse, efficacy of treatments and use of risk assessments, to name a few) are driving best practice and our understanding of the issues raised in this chapter.

References

Alexander R & Cooray S (2003) Diagnosis of personality disorders in learning disability. *British Journal of Psychiatry* **182** (Suppl. 44) s28-31.

Alexander RT, Crouch K, Halstead S & Piachaud J (2006) Long-term outcome from a medium secure services for people with intellectual disability. *Journal of Intellectual Disability Research* **50** 305-315.

American Psychiatric Association (1980) *Diagnostic and Statistical Manual of Mental Disorders* (3rd edition). Washington, DC: American Psychiatric Association.

Arseneault L, Cannon M, Poulton R, Murray R, Caspi A & Moffitt TE (2002) Cannabis use in adolescence and risk for adult psychosis: longitudinal prospective study. *British Medical Journal* **325** 1212–1213.

Barrowcliff AL (2007) Cognitive-behavioural therapy for command hallucinations and intellectual disability: A case study. *Journal of Applied Research in Intellectual Disabilities* **21** (3) 236-245.

Branford D (1994) A study of the prescribing for people with learning disabilities living in the community and in National Health Service care. *Journal of Intellectual Disability Research* **38** 577-586.

Cooper SA, Smiley E, Morrison J, Williamson A & Allan L (2007) Mental ill-health in adults with intellectual disabilities: prevalence and associated factors. *British Journal of Psychiatry* **109** 27-35.

Department of Health (1999) *The National Service Framework for Mental Health: Modern Standards and Service Models*. London: Department of Health.

Flynn A, Matthews H, & Hollins S (2002) Validity of the diagnosis of personality disorder of adults with learning disability and severe behavioural problems. *British Journal of Psychiatry* **180** 543-546.

Grettan HM, McBride M, Hare RD, Shaughensey RO & Kumka G (2001) Psychopathy and recidivism in adolescent sex offenders. *Criminal Justice and Behaviour* **28** 427-429.

Hare RD (1991) *The Hare Psychopathy Checklist – revised*. Toronto, ON: Multi Health Systems.

Hodgins S, Menick SA, Brennan PA, Schlusinger F & Engberg M (1996) Mental disorder and crime: Evidence from a Danish birth cohort. *Archives of General Psychiatry* **53** 489-96.

Hollins S & Sinason V (2000) Psychotherapy, learning disabilities and trauma: new perspectives. *British Journal of Psychiatry* **176** 32-36.

Huxley A, Taggart L, Baker G, Castillo L & Barnes D (2007) Substance misuse amongst people with learning disabilities. *Learning Disability Today* **7** (3) 34-38.

Klimecki MR, Jenkinson J & Wilson L (1994) A study of recidivism among offenders with an intellectual disability. *Australian and New Zealand Journal of Developmental Disabilities* **19** (3) 209-19.

Lindsay W, Machie A, Baty F, Smith A & Millar S (1994) The consistency of reports about feelings and emotions for people with learning difficulties. *Journal of Intellectual Disability Research* **38** 61-66.

Lindsay WR, Hogue T, Taylor JT, Mooney P, Steptoe L, Johnston S, O'Brien G & Smith AHW (2006a) Two studies on the prevalence and validity of personality disorder in three forensic intellectual disability samples. *The Journal of Forensic Psychiatry & Psychology* **17** (3) 485-506.

Lindsay WR, Howells L & Pitcaithly D (1993) Cognitive therapy for depression with individuals with intellectual disabilities. *British Journal of Medical Psychology* **66** 135-41.

Lindsay WR, Neilson C & Lawrenson H (1997) Cognitive-behaviour therapy for anxiety in people with learning disabilities. In: B Stenfert Kroese, D Dagnan and K Loumidis (Eds) *Cognitive Behaviour Therapy for People with Learning Disabilities* (pp124-140). London: Routledge.

Lindsay WR, Steele L, Smith AHW, Quinn K & Allan R (2006b) A community forensic intellectual disability service: Twelve year follow up of referrals, analysis of referral patterns and assessment of harm reduction. *Legal and Criminological Psychology* **11** 113-130.

Link BG, Stueve A & Phelan J (1998) Psychotic symptoms and violent behaviours: probing the components of 'threat/control-override' symptoms. *Social Psychiatry and Psychiatric Epidemiology* **33** S55-60.

Mann AH, Jenkins R, Cutting JC, & Cowen PJ (1981) The development and use of a standardized assessment of abnormal personality. *Psychological Medicine* **11** 839-847.

McGillicuddy NB (2006) A review of substance use research among those with mental retardation. *Mental Retardation and Developmental Disabilities Research Review* **12** 41-47.

Morrissey C, Hogue TE, Mooney P, Lindsay WR, Steptoe L, Taylor J, & Johnston S (2005) Applicability, reliability and validity of the Psychopathy Checklist-Revised in offenders with intellectual disabilities: Some initial findings. *International Journal of Forensic Mental Health* **4** (2) 207-220.

Morrissey C, Mooney P, Hogue PD, Lindsay W & Taylor JL (2007) Predictive validity of the PCL-R for offenders with intellectual disability in a high security hospital: treatment process. *Journal of intellectual and developmental disability* **32** (2) 123-133.

National Institute for Mental Health in England (2003a) *Personality Disorder Capabilities Framework: Breaking the Cycle of Rejection*. London: Department of Health.

National Institute for Mental Health in England (2003b) *Personality Disorder: No longer a diagnosis of exclusion*. London: Department of Health.

Oathamshaw SC & Haddock G (2006) Do people with intellectual disabilities and psychosis have the cognitive skills required to undertake cognitive behavioural therapy? *Journal of Applied Research in Intellectual Disabilities* **19** 35-46.

Prout TH & Nowak-Drabik KM (2003) Psychotherapy with persons who have intellectual disabilities: an evaluation of effectiveness. *American Journal on Intellectual Disabilities* **108** 82-93.

Reid, AH & Ballinger BR (1987) Personality Disorder in Mental Handicap. *Psychological Medicine* **17** 983-987.

Singleton N, Bumpstead R, O'Brien M, Lee A & Meltzer H (2001) *Psychiatric Morbidity among Adults Living in Private Households, 2000*. London: TSO.

Singleton N, Meltzer H, Gatward R, Coid J & Deasy D (1998) *Psychiatric Morbidity among Prisoners in England and Wales*. London: ONS.

Smith H, White T & Walker P (2008) Offending in the learning disabled population: a retrospective audit of Tayside learning disability service court reports. *Medicine, Science & the Law* **48** (1) 31-6.

Sovner R (1986) Limiting factors in the use of DSM-III criteria with mentally ill/mentally retarded persons. *Psychopharmacology Bulletin* **22** 1055-1059.

Taggart L, Huxley A & Baker G (2008) Alcohol and illicit drug misuse in people with learning disabilities: implications for research and service development. *Advances in Mental Health in Learning Disabilities* **2** (1) 11-21.

Taylor PJ, Leese M, Williams D, Butwell M, Daly R & Larkin E (1998) Mental disorder and violence: a special (high security) hospital study. *British Journal of Psychiatry* **172** 218-226.

Turner TH (1989) Schizophrenia and mental handicap – an historical review and implications for future research. *Psychological Medicine* **19** 301-314.

Tyrer P, Oliver-Africano PC, Ahmed Z, Bouras N, Cooray S, Deb S, Murphy D, Hare M, Meade M, Reece B, Kramo K, Bhaumik S, Harley D, Regan A, Thomas D, Rao B, North B, Eliahoo J, Karatela S, Soni A & Crawford M (2008) Risperidone, haloperidol, and placebo in the treatment of aggressive challenging behaviour in patients with intellectual disability: a randomized controlled trial. *Lancet* **371** 57-63.

Whitehouse RM, Tudway JA, Look R & Stenfert Kroese B (2006) Adapting individual psychotherapy for individuals with intellectual disabilities: a comparative review of the cognitive-behavioural and psychodynamic literature. *Journal of Applied Research in Intellectual Disabilities* **19** (1) 55-65.

World Health Organization (1992) *The ICD-10 International Classification of Mental and Behavioural Disorders. Clinical Descriptions and Diagnostic Guidelines*. Geneva: World Health Organization.

World Health Organization (1993) *The ICD–10 International Classification of Mental and Behavioural Disorders: Diagnostic Criteria for Research*. Geneva: World Health Organization.

Zisook S, Byrd D, Kuck J & Jeste DV (1995) Command hallucinations in outpatients with schizophrenia. *Journal of Clinical Psychiatry* **56** 462-5.

Section 3

Part B

Neurodevelopmental disorders and offending

Alex Ward, Ailsa Russell and Kiriakos Xenitidis

Introduction

This chapter will initially define autistic spectrum disorders (also known as autistic spectrum conditions) before moving on to explore the link between autism spectrum disorders and offending behaviour. It will also provide a review of the current literature.

Autism spectrum disorder

Autism spectrum disorder (ASD) refers to a lifelong developmental disorder defined by the key diagnostic characteristics specified in section F84 of the *International Classification of Diseases, 10th edition (ICD-10)* (World Health Organization, 1992), on pervasive developmental disorders (PDDs). ASDs are defined by qualitative impairments in reciprocal social interaction and communication, and a restricted, repetitive or stereotyped pattern of behaviours and interests. These characteristic features are commonly termed the 'triad of impairments' (see **Figure 3B.1**) and are evident before the age of 36 months, persisting throughout life.

Figure 3B.1: Triad of impairments

The triad of impairments has also been used to better understand the association between the core characteristics of ASDs and offending behaviour.

1. Qualitative abnormalities in reciprocal social interaction may lead to:

- lack of understanding of societal rules and norms
- social naivety
- deliberate exploitation by others and vulnerability to peer influences
- social perception and history of bullying may lead to misinterpretation of others' intentions as malicious/hostile, causing negative reactions.

Figure 3B.1: Triad of impairments

2. Communication abnormalities may contribute to:

- difficulties expressing emotional states and needs or wishes, which may lead to frustration and inappropriate/maladaptive attempts to communicate
- language abnormalities and literal understanding of language may result in misunderstanding, leading to contravention of societal norms/laws.

3. Stereotyped behaviours and restricted interests might cause difficulties as:

- the pursuit of a special interest with morbid qualities (for example, poisons/weapons) may bring people into conflict with the criminal justice system,
- agitation/aggressive outbursts as a result of disruption to routine
- rigid interpretation of rules.

Many differing labels and terms are used to describe the various ASDs. These include childhood autism, atypical autism, high functioning autism and Asperger's syndrome. For the purposes of this chapter, ASD will refer to all adults who have an autism spectrum disorder, remembering that this encompasses a variety of groups in terms of intellectual, communicative and social functioning. What they all share is one or more of the core characteristics of autism.

ASD can occur in the context of a learning disability but it is as likely to be observed in people with intellectual function in the average range. In the latter group, there can be a very diffuse pattern of cognitive and functional skills, with some abilities being above average, and some abilities falling in the learning disability range. To this end, it is sometimes not very meaningful to attach a summary IQ score to people with an ASD as this does not often reflect the quite significant difficulties they experience in their lives. It can also be difficult to decide whether they should be offered services by community mental health or learning disability services.

There is not a great deal of research examining criminal and offending behaviour in people with ASD. Most studies have looked at people with Asperger's syndrome (AS), although some have looked at broader and mixed ASD diagnostic populations. Studies of offending behaviour in people with childhood autism are very rare. It is likely that the same issues that affect other populations with learning disabilities in respect to criminal behaviour are relevant here.

ASD and offending behaviour

The relationship between offending behaviour and ASD is not fully understood and is likely to be a complex one. Caution should be used when interpreting findings from research studies in this area, as studies will have used different diagnostic criteria and therefore may be drawing conclusions about different groups. Population base rates of ASD continue to fluctuate, which can also make comparisons unreliable.

It is not known whether people who have an ASD are more or less likely to commit criminal offences than the general population, although the limited evidence would suggest that there is an increased association. We do know, however, that there have been individuals with ASD who have committed offences, sometimes serious, which have resulted in criminal proceedings and imprisonment, or detention in psychiatric care with conditions of security. People with ASD have been identified in the UK's three special hospitals, Rampton Hospital, Broadmoor Hospital and Ashworth Hospital (Hare *et al*, 1999). Currently, there is no information about the number of adults with ASD within the UK prison system.

Scragg & Shah, (1994) reported that the prevalence of Asperger's syndrome in the population detained in Broadmoor Hospital was greater than the prevalence of Asperger's syndrome in the general population. Hare *et al* (1999) examined individuals with the broader label of ASD within all three maximum security special hospitals. They found that people with an ASD stayed in the hospitals for an average of 8.5 years – between two and three years longer than other patients. It was noted that, although they only form a small group within the hospitals, people with an ASD pose unique challenges in terms of management, treatment and eventual placement, which may reflect their increased length of stay.

In terms of community forensic samples, in a study of juveniles referred for forensic psychiatric evaluation in Sweden, Siponmaa *et al* (2001) identified rates of pervasive developmental disorder (PDD) that were 15-fold above the incidence in the general population. In Denmark, a large case control study recently published by Mouridsen *et al* (2008) describes over 300 child psychiatric inpatients with a diagnosis of ASD who were followed up in adulthood. Of the 300 people with a diagnosis of ASD, 9% had been subject to a criminal conviction compared to 18% in the comparison groups.

Haskins & Silva (2006) summarised the literature relating to Asperger's syndrome and criminal behaviour and concluded that, based on preliminary findings, there is an over-representation of high functioning autism spectrum disorders among criminal populations compared to the rate in the general population.

Patterns of offending behaviour

In addition to looking at how many people within forensic populations have an ASD, studies have also sought to find out whether particular patterns of offending behaviour are associated with ASD. As well as the small number of group studies, conclusions have been drawn from individual cases and case series studies.

Arson

There are some case descriptions of firesetting in adolescents (Everall & LeCouteur, 1990) and in adults with ASD (Barry-Walsh & Mullen, 2004). Within the group studies that have been mentioned, a relatively high incidence of firesetting is established. For example, Woodbury-Smith *et al* (2005) compared 21 adults with ASD and offending behaviour, with 23 adults with ASD without offending behaviour, to 23 healthy controls. Of the 21 adult offenders with ASD, just over a quarter were convicted of arson. In the adolescent study, Siponmaa *et al* (2001) reported that of the 16 cases in their group who had committed arson, 10 (63%) had a diagnosis of an ASD. In the three UK special hospitals study, Hare *et al* (1999) identified five (16%) of the autistic spectrum group who had an index offence of arson, compared to 10% of the total special hospital population. More recently, a case control study by Mouridsen *et al* (2008) comparing individuals with Asperger's syndrome to a matched control group, found arson to be the only offending behaviour to reach statistical significance, with five (4.4%) of the Asperger's group having convictions of arson compared to none from the controls.

Sexual offending

Sexual offending and stalking behaviour have also been described in case studies (Chesterman & Rutter 1993; Milton *et al*, 2002; Kohn *et al*, 1998; Stoke & Newton, 2004). A typology of 'stalkers' in the psychiatric forensic literature (Mullen *et al*, 2001) highlights five types of stalker, of which the 'incompetent suitor' may be most applicable to people with Asperger's syndrome. These people may inappropriately intrude on someone when seeking a date or brief sexual encounter, as they often lack appropriate courting and social skills. In general, people who have been convicted of stalking have been found to be typically male, underachieving in terms of employment, of average intelligence, and characterised by isolation, loneliness and social ineptness.

In their study of the three special hospitals, Hare *et al* (1999) found a very low level of sexual offending in the autism group compared to the rest of the hospital population. Haskins and Silva (2006) conclude that a defective capacity to attain socially sanctioned sexual release can underlie certain sexual offences in some individuals with a high functioning autism spectrum disorder. However, it is important not to assume that sexual offending in this population is due only to social impairments. A thorough assessment is needed (as outlined in **Section 4A: Working with sexual offenders with learning disabilities**) as the offending behaviour may or may not be related specifically to deficits associated with ASD.

Violence/aggression

Acts of violence and violent offending have not been specifically studied in this population but, again, there are case reports that highlight this phenomenon in people with ASD (Mawson *et al*, 1985; Baron-Cohen, 1998); and, for a critique, see Ghaziuddin *et al* (1991). Aggressive behaviour may occur but not result in criminal proceedings. Often, aggressive behaviour is seen to take place within the family context and therefore the likelihood of charges being brought, within this context, is reduced.

Other

There have been a number of high profile cases where an individual's circumscribed interest has brought them into conflict with the law. For example, many newspaper reports have been written about Darius McCollum, notorious for having spent over a third of his adult life in prison as a result of his obsessional interest in the New York subway system, which has led him to impersonate drivers, steal trains and commit numerous other offences related to the transit authority.

Reasons for offending

Research has investigated a number of domains of cognition as the central deficit in ASD (see **Figure 3B.2**). There has been considerable speculation about factors associated with ASD and their potential relationship with offending behaviour, although much remains theoretical. *The Reed Report* (Department of Health and Home Office, 1992) and Howlin (1997) propose that common reasons for offending in ASD include deliberate exploitation by others, aggressive behaviour often as a result of disruption to routine, antisocial behaviour through a lack of understanding, communication difficulties, a lack of appreciation of social cues, and obsessional tendencies/morbid interests.

Figure 3B.2: Central deficits

1. **Theory of mind (ToM):** this refers to the ability to understand and make inferences about the mental states (ie. thoughts, beliefs, intentions and emotions) of others. Research has identified that many (but by no means all) people with ASD show impairments in ToM tests (Happé, 1994). This may serve as a mitigating factor in criminal behaviour, or increase the likelihood of future crimes due to lack of remorse and victim empathy.

2. **Face processing:** neurobiological research has identified deficits in face processing in adults with ASD. Perceiving the emotional reaction of others accurately can provide important clues about the appropriateness of our behaviour in an interpersonal context. If we are not able to accurately judge the impact a situation is having on another person, we may not modify our behaviour accordingly.

3. **Executive function (EF):** this refers to a complex set of neuropsychological functions that essentially represent the 'supervisory' system of the brain. EF is the set of cognitive abilities that underlie flexible, goal-directed behaviour, including planned behaviour, focused and sustained attention, self-monitoring and correction, inhibition of inappropriate behaviours, and forming abstract concepts (Liss *et al*, 2001). EF deficits can be associated with significant changes in behaviour and personality. Primarily, people can become impulsive, not plan effectively or not think through the consequences of their actions.

Empathic deficiencies

A lack of empathy has been reported to be linked with offending behaviour in ASD, specifically a proneness to violence (Tantum, 1991). Murrie *et al* (2002), from their small case series, state that deficient empathy is a central feature among the Asperger's syndrome patients who commit crime.

A lack of empathy is known to play a role in the offending behaviour of psychopaths. The association between ASD and psychopathy is little studied. However, a recent paper (Rogers *et al*, 2006) proposes that in some cases the callous acts seen in a small number of people with an ASD may represent a 'double hit' of impairment in empathic response over and above that seen in ASD alone. This association of features seen in psychopathy has been studied by Murphy (2007) at Broadmoor Hospital. He assessed 13 male patients at the hospital, all with a diagnosis of Asperger's syndrome using the Hare Psychopathy

Checklist Revised (PCL-R) (Hare, 1991). The results showed a variation in some individual profiles of scores but that all the total scores in this sample were below the American and British cut-off scores for psychopathy. This would indicate that serious offending behaviour in adults with ASDs that requires management within a maximum security hospital setting, can occur in this population in the absence of a comorbid psychopathic disorder.

Practice issues

As we have now seen, a small proportion of adults with an ASD do come into contact with the criminal justice system. Consideration needs to be given to some of the issues that will play a role as they progress through the criminal process. *Autism: A guide for criminal justice professionals*, published by the National Autistic Society (2005) aims to provide information to criminal justice professionals who may come into contact with someone with an ASD, whether they be a victim, a witness, a suspect or an offender. It offers advice regarding the interview process, including environmental adaptations, how to conduct the interview and how to interpret the response. The use of an 'appropriate adult' (AA) in these situations should always be considered. Allen *et al* (2008) welcomed adaptations to the conviction process to help reduce the difficulties encountered by the individuals as they negotiate the criminal justice system, as described by both Barry-Walsh & Mullen (2004) and Mayes (2003) in their discussion on issues relating to competence to stand trial, capacity related defences, mitigation in sentencing and evidentiary issues.

Forensic psychologists and psychiatrists are commonly asked to ascertain the reliability of statements made by suspects to the police during questioning, and to assess an individual's vulnerability to providing information that is inaccurate, unreliable and misleading during police interview. Interrogative suggestibility is 'the extent to which, within a closed social interaction, people come to accept messages communicated during formal questioning, as the result of which their subsequent behavioural response is affected' (Gudjonsson & Clark, 1986). North *et al* (2008) compared 26 individuals with high functioning ASD, and 27 gender and IQ matched controls on measures of interrogative suggestibility and compliance. There were no significant between-group differences on the measures of suggestibility, but the group with ASD were rated as significantly more compliant than the controls. Individuals with ASD may be more eager to please or to avoid conflict and confrontation than controls, and may be more prone to respond compliantly to requests and demands.

In some of the case reports mentioned, it has been the offending behaviour that has led to the diagnosis of an ASD being made. It can be expected that an earlier diagnosis and subsequent intervention may have prevented these individuals from committing offences and becoming involved with the criminal justice system.

Treatment issues

There are no established reasons why standard approaches to treating offending behaviour in other groups should not be applied to people with ASD. Adaptations may be required to talking therapies, with greater use of visual materials, affective education, a more directive approach and greater involvement of parents/carers as co-therapists required when delivering psychological treatment within a cognitive behavioural framework (Anderson & Morris, 2006).

Interventions should be based on individual case formulations, where the interaction between autism-specific impairments and offending behaviours is clearly outlined. Intervention is likely to require a multidisciplinary approach.

Comprehensive assessment of the characteristics of the person's ASD should be conducted, including a clear understanding of their cognitive profile and strengths and weaknesses, theory of mind abilities, manifestation of the ASD in terms of special interests, social interaction and communication skills, history of interpersonal relationships, experience of bullying, sources of anxiety and anger, preferred routines and structure etc. The Autism Diagnostic Observation Schedule (ADOS) (Lord *et al*, 2000) can be a very useful tool in measuring some aspects of an individual's function.

Ideally, a functional analytic model (eg. Sturmey, 1996) should be used to understand the offence. This will include highlighting the antecedent factors, setting events and consequences, as well as describing the behaviour in detail. It should not neglect the role that internal events, interests and preoccupations may play in driving the offending behaviour. Where antecedent factors are thought to have played a significant role, managing the environment, being alert for similar risk factors, educating the individual about the formulation and developing more adaptive coping strategies will be important. Particular attention should be paid to the potentially stress-reducing nature of the consequences of offending behaviour in this group. For example, a stressful, unpredictable living situation may be greatly relieved by removal to a custodial setting, where the environment, although aversive, is also highly structured and predictable.

Where an individual's particular interest or preoccupation has played a part in driving the offending behaviour, the person will need direction and support to channel their interests more adaptively (for example, in an employment situation where their in-depth knowledge of a subject would be an asset to an employer).

Generalising rules and interventions across situations can be an issue with this group. To this end, trying to make rules for 'staying safe' as concrete as possible is useful. Ongoing interventions may be required in terms of making rules and guidelines situation-specific and approaching each novel situation as precisely that – novel.

With regards to risk monitoring, it has been our experience that individuals often find it difficult to monitor their own risk in a self-generated fashion. To this end, we have developed idiographic risk monitoring tools in collaboration with an individual. Here, at regular intervals an individual is prompted to notice their thoughts/feelings/urges and current worries/problems, and also rate whether or not they consider themselves to be at risk. We have found that it is more successful when carers support this process, rather than expecting an individual to manage it alone. Use of a visually anchored, written tool is generally more helpful than relying solely on verbal interviews.

In terms of pharmacological interventions, there have been only a few studies involving adults with ASD, none of whom have been classed as offenders. Low dose Risperidone was found to be more effective in reducing interfering repetitive behaviours, as well as aggression towards self, property and others than placebo. Fluvoxamine and Fluoxetine have been shown to have similar effects on behaviour when compared with placebo (see McDougle *et al* (2006) for a review).

ADHD and offending behaviour

Like other neurodevelopmental disorders, the validity of the diagnosis of attention deficit hyperactivity disorder (ADHD) in adulthood has been the subject of much debate (Toone, 2004). In addition, ADHD symptoms are more prevalent in people with other neurodevelopmental disorders, such as learning disabilities and autistic spectrum disorders. However, learning disabilities and autistic spectrum disorders have often been used as exclusionary criteria for the diagnosis of ADHD. The validity of paediatric diagnosis of ADHD in the context of comorbidity has recently been established (Antshel *et al*, 2006). In terms of the prevalence of the condition, although a wide range of rates has been quoted, depending on age, setting and diagnostic criteria used, a lifespan prevalence of 4% is generally accepted (Nutt *et al*, 2007).

The relationship between ADHD and behavioural disorders is a complex one in terms of aetiological mechanisms but at a descriptive level it is well established (Satterfield *et al*, 1994). In a meta-analysis of 20 ADHD studies, Pratt *et al* (2002) report a strong positive association between ADHD symptoms and criminality or delinquency. Epidemiological studies suggest that adults with a history of childhood ADHD are at higher risk of being involved with the police (Rasmussen & Gillberg, 2000). When ADHD co-exists with learning disabilities, both the diagnosis and the treatment of the former condition is more complex. In a long-term follow-up study, Handen *et al* (1997) reported that both ADHD symptoms and behavioural problems tend to persist to an extent despite pharmacotherapy. Interestingly, Lindsay *et al* (2009) in their recent case note review of 477 individuals referred to forensic learning disability services, found that the highest reported diagnostic category for those both referred and accepted into services was ADHD/conduct disorder.

It has also been reported that adults with ADHD are over-represented in prison populations (Curran & Fitzgerald, 1999). When ADHD symptoms rather than the full syndrome are considered, this difference is of course greater. It is not clear to what extent this over-representation is due to adults with ADHD (like other neurodevelopmental disorders) being more easily caught than their peers without attention deficits (Young, 2007).

The characteristics of offenders with ADHD have been the subject of debate. In particular, the male over-representation amongst ADHD sufferers seems to be less strong than initially reported. There is some evidence that women tend to commit more minor offences compared to men (Brassett-Grundy & Butler, 2004). In terms of personality characteristics, antisocial personality disorder traits may confound the relationship between ADHD and crime. There is a known association between conduct disorder in childhood and antisocial personality in adulthood. Most studies report that criminal behaviour is associated more with hyperactivity and impulsivity, rather than inattentive symptoms.

With regards to the characteristics of the offences, the evidence is inconclusive but it appears that public order and property crime is more common than violent crime in people with ADHD. Offences are typically linked with reckless behaviour, are unplanned and are commonly motivated by a desire to meet an immediate demand.

A number of underlying mechanisms have been proposed to explain the link between ADHD symptoms and offending behaviour. These include poor response tolerance, low boredom threshold, impatience and impulsivity. Novelty-seeking may result in risk-taking and thrill-seeking behaviour such as reckless driving. Poor emotional regulation, including anger control, is often involved in violent crime. Impulsivity may also lead to sexually disinhibited behaviour and sexual offending.

From a clinical practice point of view, mental health professionals may be requested to consider the diagnosis of ADHD in an offender (or accused) with learning disabilities. Moreover, professionals may be asked to provide court reports in relation to criminal or civil proceedings for adults with ADHD. A significant proportion of these people are likely to have co-existing learning disabilities. These requests are often around issues of fitness to plead, criminal responsibility, mitigating factors for sentence and modifications in the trial process for defendants with ADHD (Young, 2007). Awareness of the conceptual issues involved and clinical experience in both the diagnosis and treatment (psychological and pharmacological) of adults with ADHD with varying degrees of intellectual impairment is essential for appropriate disposal and management, especially in the interface between clinical practice and the criminal justice system.

Conclusion

People with ASD can vary considerably in terms of language, general intellectual ability, life skills and social function. Currently, there is no evidence to suggest that treatment approaches for offenders in the general population do not work for people with ASD, provided this is based on individual assessment and formulation.

Although the many case studies and small series reviewed here report on a potential association between ASDs and offending behaviour, there is no evidence that people with ASD commit a greater number of criminal offences than people without ASD. There is, however, emerging evidence for a selective pattern of offending behaviour, with some clinical studies suggesting that firesetting may be more prevalent. It has also been reported that crimes that are 'odd' or in which there appears to be little gain may be pointers towards an ASD offender.

In some cases (Schwartz-Watts, 2005), it has been observed that it is serious offending behaviour that leads to a diagnosis being made. This may highlight that there are many more offenders within the general offending population, and potentially in prison, who have an ASD but who have not yet been given the diagnosis. It is well established that people who have an ASD do better in environments where there is predictability, structure and routine. Prison environments and their regimes are typical examples of such situations. People who have an ASD may settle quickly within this environment and their mental health needs may not become obvious to the authorities. Of concern is that they may be a particularly vulnerable group within this setting.

There is a growing literature regarding ADHD and offending behaviour in the mainstream population, which is likely to be applicable to offenders with learning disabilities; however, there is little evidence as yet to support this assumption. Nevertheless, recent research suggests that a significant proportion of individuals presenting to forensic learning disability services may have ADHD. Clinicians therefore need to consider the presence and role of ADHD in the offending behaviour and the treatment needs of this population.

Future directions for research should include studies based on prison populations and studies to develop a better understanding of offending behaviour within this population and treatment strategies to reduce reoffending.

References

Allen D, Evans C, Hider A, Hawkins S, Peckett H & Morgan H (2008) Offending Behaviour in Adults with Asperger Syndrome. *Journal of Autism and Developmental Disorders* **38** (4).

Anderson S & Morris J (2006) Cognitive behaviour therapy for people with Asperger Syndrome. *Behavioural and Cognitive Psychotherapy* **34** 293-303.

Antshel K, Phillips M, Gordon G, Barklay R & Farone SV (2006) Is ADHD a valid disorder in children with intellectual delays? *Clinical Psychology Review* **25** (5) 555-572.

Baron-Cohen S (1998) An Assessment of a Young Man with Asperger's Syndrome. *Journal of Child Psychiatry and Psychology* **29** 351-360.

Barry-Walsh J & Mullen PE (2004) Forensic Aspects of Asperger's Syndrome. *Journal of Child Psychiatry and Psychology* **1** (15) 96-107.

Brassett-Grundy A & Butler N (2004) Prevalence and adult outcomes of attention-deficit/hyperactivity disorder: Evidence from a 30-year prospective longitudinal study. *Bedford group for lifecourse and statistical studies occasional paper: No. 2*. London: Institute of Education, University of London.

Chesterman P & Rutter C (1993) Case Report: Asperger's Syndrome and Sexual Offending. *Journal of Forensic Psychiatry* **4** (3) 555-562.

Curran S & Fitzgerald M (1999) Attention deficit and hyperactivity disorder in the prison population. *American Journal of Psychiatry* **156** 1664-1665.

Department of Health and Home Office (1992) *The Reed Report into Mentally Disordered Offenders and Others who Require Similar Services* (CM2088). London: HMSO.

Everall IP & LeCouteur A (1990) Fire-setting in an adolescent boy with Asperger's Syndrome. *British Journal of Psychiatry* **157** 284-287.

Ghaziuddin M *et al* (1991) Brief report: violence in Asperger's syndrome, a critique. *Journal of Autism and Developmental Disorders* **2** (3) 349-353,

Gudjonsson GH & Clark NK (1986) Suggestibility in police interrogation: a social, psychological model. *Social Behaviour* **1** 83-104.

Handen BL, Janosky J & McAnliffe S (1997) Long-term follow-up of children with mental retardation/ borderline intellectual functioning and ADHD. *Journal of Abnormal Child Psychology* **25** (4) 287-295.

Happé F (1994) An advanced test of theory of mind: understanding of story characters' thoughts and feelings by able autistic, mentally handicapped, and normal children and adults. *Journal of Autism and Developmental Disorders* **24** 129-154.

Hare J, Gould J, Mills R & Wing L (1999) *A Preliminary Study of Individuals with Autistic Spectrum Disorders in Three Hospitals in England*. Available at: www.nas.org.uk/content/1/c4/38/68/3hospitals.pdf (accessed July 2009).

Hare R (1991) *Hare Psychopathy Checklist – Revised (PCL-R)*. Toronto, ON: Multi Health Systems.

Haskins B & Silva JA (2006) Asperger's disorder and criminal behaviour: forensic psychiatric considerations. *The Journal of the American Academy of Psychiatry and the Law* **34** 374-384.

Howlin P (1997) *Autism: Preparing for adulthood*. London: Routledge.

Kohn Y, Fehum T, Ratzoni G & Apter A (1998) Aggression and sexual offence in Asperger's Syndrome. *The Israel Journal of Psychiatry* **35** 293.

Lindsay WR, Holland A, Taylor J, O'Brien G & Carson D (2009) *Risk, diagnostic and childhood adversity information for offenders with intellectual disability*. The 7th European Congress of Mental Health in Intellectual Disability, Amsterdam.

Liss M, Fein D, Allen D, Dunn M, Feinstein C, Morris R, Waterhouse L & Rapin I (2001) Executive functioning in high-functioning children with autism. *Journal of Child Psychology and Psychiatry* **42** 261–270.

Lord C, Risi S, Lambrecht L, Cook EH, Leventhal BL & DiLavore PC (2000) The Autism diagnostic observation schedule-generic: a standard measure of social and communication deficits associated with the spectrum of autism. *Journal of Autism and Developmental Disorders* **30** (3) 205-223.

Mawson D, Grounds A & Tantam D (1985) Violence and Asperger's syndrome: a case study. *British Journal of Psychiatry* **147** 566-569.

Mayes TA (2003) Persons with autism and criminal Justice: core concepts and leading cases. *Journal of Positive Behaviour Interventions* **5** (2) 92-100.

McDougle CJ, Stigler KA, Erickson CA & Posey DJ (2006) Pharmacology of autism. *Clinical Neuroscience Research* **6** 179-188.

Milton J, Duggan C, Lathan A & Tantam D (2002) Case history of co-morbid Asperger's syndrome and paraphilic behaviour. *Medicine, Science and Law* **42** 237-244.

Mouridsen SE, Rich B, Isager T & Nedergaard NJ (2008) Pervasive developmental disorders and criminal behaviour. a case control study. *International Journal of Offender Therapy and Comparative Criminology* **52** (2) 196-205.

Mullen PE, Pathé M & Purcell R (2001) The management of stalkers. *Advances in Psychiatric Treatment* **7** 335-342.

Murphy D (2007) Hare Psychopathy Checklist Revised profiles of male patients with Asperger's syndrome detained in high security psychiatric care. *The Journal of Forensic Psychiatry and Psychology* **18** (1) 120-126.

Murrie DC, Warren JI, Kristiansson M & Dietz PD (2002) Asperger's Syndrome in Forensic settings. *International Journal of Forensic Mental Health* **1** (1) 59-70.

National Autistic Society (2005) *Autism: A guide for criminal justice professionals*. Available at: www.nas.org.uk/nas/jsp/polopoly.jsp?a=8528&d=471 (accessed August 2009).

North AS, Russell AJ & Gudjonsson GH (2008) High functioning autism spectrum disorders: an investigation of psychological vulnerabilities during interrogative interview. *Journal of Forensic Psychiatry and Psychology* **19** (3) 323-334.

Nutt DJ, Fone K, Asherson P *et al* (2007) Evidence-based guidelines for management of attention-deficit/hyperactivity disorder in adolescents in transition to adult services and in adults: recommendations from the British Association for Psychopharmacology. *Journal of Psychopharmacology* **21** (1) 10-41. Originally published online, 8 November 2006, at: http://jop.sagepub.com/cgi/content/abstract/21/1/10 (accessed July 2009).

Pratt TC, Cullen FT, Blevins KR & Unnever LD (2002) The relationship of attention deficit hyperactivity disorder to crime and delinquency: a meta-analysis, *International Journal of Police Science and Management* **4** 344–360.

Rasmussen P & Gillberg C (2000) Natural outcome of ADHD with developmental coordination disorder at age 22 years: a controlled, longitudinal, community-based study. *Journal of the American Academy of Child and Adolescent Psychiatry* **39** 1424-1431.

Rogers J, Viding E, Blair RJ, Frith U & Happé F (2006) Autism spectrum disorder and psychopathy: shared cognitive underpinnings or a double hit? *Psychological Medicine* **36** 1789-1798.

Satterfield JH, Swanson JM, Schell A & Lee F (1994). Prediction of antisocial behavior in attention-deficit hyperactivity disorder boys from aggression/defiance scores. *Journal of the American Academy of Child and Adolescent Psychiatry* **33** 185-190.

Schwartz-Watts DM (2005) Asperger's Disorder and Murder. *Journal of American Academy Psychiatry Law* **33** 390-393.

Scragg P & Shah A (1994) Prevalence of Asperger's Syndrome in a Secure Hospital. *British Journal of Psychiatry* **165** 679-682.

Siponmaa L, Kristiansson M, Jonsson C, Nydén A & Gillberg C (2001) Juvenile and young adult mentally disordered offenders: the role of child neuropsychiatric disorders. *Journal of American Academy of Psychiatry and Law* **29** 420-426.

Stoke M & Newton N (2004) Letter to the editor. *Autism – The International Journal of Research and Practice* **1** 335-339.

Sturmey P (1996) *Functional Analysis in Clinical Psychology*. Chichester: John Wiley & Sons Ltd.

Tantum D (1991) Asperger syndrome in adulthood. In: U Frith (Ed) *Autism and Asperger Syndrome* (pp147-183). Cambridge: Cambridge University Press.

Toone B (2004) Attention deficit hyperactivity disorder in adulthood. *Journal of Neurology, Neurosurgery & Psychiatry* **75** 523-525.

Woodbury-Smith MR, Clare ICH, Holland AJ, Kearns A, Staufenberg E & Watson P (2005) A case-control study of offenders with high functioning autistic spectrum disorders. *Journal of Forensic Psychiatry and Psychology* **16** (4) 747-763.

World Health Organization (1992) *The ICD-10 International Classification of Mental and Behavioural Disorders*. Geneva: World Health Organization.

Young S (2007) Forensic aspects of ADHD. In: M Fitzgerald, M Bellgrove and M Gill (Eds.) *Handbook of Attention Deficit Hyperactivity Disorder*. Chichester: John Wiley and Sons.

Section 4

Working with offenders

Section 4
Part A

Working with sexual offenders with learning disabilities

Christopher Bennett and Jayne Henry

Introduction

The link between sexual offending and learning disabilities is a complex one, and one that is often poorly understood. Much has been written about people with learning disabilities being the victims of sexual assault (eg. Craft, 1993; McCabe *et al*, 1994; McCarthy & Thompson, 1994; Murphy, 2007) but to date relatively little has been written about men with learning disabilities who engage in sexual offending. Although there are some similar characteristics between non-disabled men and men with learning disabilities who sexually offend, there are also a number of specific factors relating to men with learning disabilities who commit sexual offences.

Definitions of sexual offending

The term 'sexual offending' encompasses a wide range of different sexually offensive behaviours covering both contact offences (ie. where there is physical contact between the perpetrator and the victim, for example, vaginal and anal rape, forced oral sex, touching of sexual body parts) and non-contact offences (ie. where no physical contact takes place between the perpetrator and victim, for example, voyeurism, exhibitionism, making obscene telephone calls and, more recently, downloading obscene images from the internet).

In terms of formal definitions of sexual abuse, many different ideas have been put forward, all with a slightly different emphasis. However, as Murphy (2007) states, 'they [the definitions] all share the idea of sexual behaviour perpetrated either without the victim's consent or with a victim who is defined as not able to consent'. Brown & Turk (1992) state that a victim cannot give consent if they either do not understand what it is they are consenting to or are vulnerable to pressure in a particular situation to give valid consent.

McCarthy & Thompson (1994) make the distinction between whether there was an intention to abuse and whether the act was experienced as abusive (**Table 4A.1**). They put forward the notion that 'it is only when sexual behaviour is neither *intended* to be abusive, nor is *experienced* as abusive, that it is justifiable to label it as something other than sexual abuse', for example, 'inappropriate sexual behaviour'. However, if a sexual act takes place that is neither intended to be abusive nor experienced as abusive, caution still needs to be exercised, as this may not necessarily be based on informed consent and could still be considered as a sexually abusive act. An example of this would be a man with learning disabilities masturbating in a public area of a residential care home in view of other residents. **Table 4A.1** provides us with a framework to understand when an act may be construed as abusive and when it may be seen as inappropriate.

Table 4A.1: Abusive or inappropriate

	There is an intention to abuse	**There is no intention to abuse**
Experienced as abuse (where the person perceives the act as abusive)	**SEXUAL ABUSE**	**SEXUAL ABUSE**
Not experienced as abuse (where the person does not perceive the act as abusive)	**SEXUAL ABUSE**	**INAPPROPRIATE SEXUAL BEHAVIOUR**

(McCarthy & Thompson, 1994)

Epidemiology

Estimating accurate prevalence rates for sexual offences perpetrated by men with learning disabilities is fraught with difficulty. Under-reporting of sexual offences by victims is recognised as having a major impact on prevalence rates. Finkelhor (1994) found that only half of the victims of childhood sexual abuse ever report the abuse. For people with learning disabilities living within supported settings, sexually offensive behaviours may be viewed as challenging behaviour rather than as offending behaviour. Direct care staff who are the victims of sexually abusive behaviour from men with learning disabilities may be reluctant to report the incident to the police. This may be linked to a belief that it is part of their role to tolerate such behaviours or that it should be tolerated because the person knows no better; or it may be based on the fear of the repercussions that reporting the incident might have, for themselves, the people they care for and for the service.

There has been some interesting research suggesting that deinstitutionalisation and the move towards community living has brought about an increase in the rates of offending among men with learning disabilities and, in particular, sexual offending. Lund (1990) identified a significant increase in offenders with mild learning disabilities receiving a first sentence in 1984 compared to 1973, and a doubling of the incidence of sexual offences over the same time period. This may be linked to sexually offensive behaviours becoming more apparent and visible within community environments compared with large, long-stay hospitals; or perhaps it is to do with the increased willingness of the criminal justice system to pursue convictions against people with learning disabilities.

Although some studies have reported high prevalence rates within this population (for example Gross (1985), who found that between 21% and 50% of offenders with learning disabilities had committed a sexual crime), other studies have found no clear evidence that the prevalence of sexual offending in men with learning disabilities is any greater than within the general population. Hayes (1991) found that only 3.7% of offenders with learning disabilities had committed a sexual offence compared with 4% of offenders without learning disabilities. However, these studies are relatively dated and have important methodological issues, such as the studies being carried out in different countries with different legal and policy frameworks.

Another issue not yet addressed in the literature is that of female sex offenders with learning disabilities. Although it is now beginning to be recognised that females can and do perpetrate sexual offences against both male and female victims, there is relatively little written about this in relation to the general population and almost nothing in relation to women with learning disabilities. Hayes (2007) has recently written about the experiences of women with learning disabilities who offend, although she makes no specific reference to women who commit sexual offences.

Theories of sexual offending

Over the past 20 years or so, a number of theories have been put forward that attempt to explain why an individual might engage in sexually offensive behaviour. Most influential amongst these have been the work of Wolf (1988) and Finkelhor (1984; 1986). Both of these theories have been used to try to make sense of sexual offending in men with learning disabilities and have led to some useful treatment approaches. More recently, approaches such as 'the good lives model' (Ward & Brown, 2004) have been adapted for use with men with learning disabilities, with some initial promising results. One of the few theories of sexual offending addressed specifically at men with learning disabilities is that of 'counterfeit deviance'.

Counterfeit deviance

(Hingsburger *et al*, 1991; Luiselli, 2000)

Counterfeit deviance has been a significant theory within the field of sexual offending, as it is thought to be the first theory that attempts to explain sexual offending in men with learning disabilities in relation to factors other than sexual deviance. Although it is not disputed that the behaviours are deviant, there is an attempt to understand them in terms of:

- limited sexual knowledge
- poor social and interpersonal skills
- lack of opportunities to establish appropriate sexual relationships
- sexual naivety.

While the counterfeit deviance theory has gained some popularity within the learning disability field, there is some evidence to suggest that men with learning disabilities who sexually offend do not necessarily have poorer sexual knowledge than other men with learning disabilities (Lindsey, 2004; Lunsky *et al*, 2007). In fact, Lunsky *et al*, found that offenders with learning disabilities who had committed more serious sexual offences demonstrated greater sexual knowledge than matched non-offenders. However, as Lindsey (2004) states, 'even if sex offenders are more knowledgeable than non-sex offenders, it does not necessarily follow that they have a comprehensive sexual knowledge'. It must also be borne in mind that having a greater level of sexual knowledge says nothing about how an individual may use this knowledge in everyday life.

Wolf's model

(Wolf, 1988)

Wolf's model sees sexual offending as a 'vicious cycle', which explains how offending becomes a repetitive pattern of behaviour. The cycle begins with the individual having poor self-esteem and a negative self-image. Expecting to be rejected by others, the individual withdraws and isolates himself. In the absence of more appropriate coping strategies, he engages in escapist fantasies, including deviant sexual fantasies, as a way of managing negative emotions. He may try to justify the deviant sexual fantasies to himself in order to avoid feelings of guilt. This leads to planning of how he may act out his deviant sexual fantasies and the targeting of a potential victim. The individual may engage in grooming behaviours in order to gain the victim's trust prior to carrying out the offence. Again, distorted thinking is used to try and excuse himself from what he is doing, for example: 'We're both enjoying ourselves, how can this be wrong?'. Following the offence, the individual has a brief period of sexual satisfaction but this is soon replaced by feelings of guilt, which then increase feelings of low self-esteem and thus the cycle begins again.

Finkelhor

(Finkelhor, 1984; 1986)

Finkelhor proposed a framework of four preconditions that need to be present for an individual to sexually offend against a child:

1. **Motivation to sexually abuse:** this includes having a strong emotional attachment and sexual attraction to children.

2. **Overcoming internal inhibitors:** this involves employing cognitive distortions or 'excuses' for the offending, such as denying the harm caused, minimising the impact on the victim or even blaming the victim for the offending.

3. **Overcoming external inhibitors:** planning how the offence will take place, selecting a victim etc.

4. **Overcoming victim's resistance:** this may be through a process of grooming behaviour where the individual befriends the child, or it may be through the use of threats and force.

This model forms the basis of the prison service's Sex Offender Treatment Programme (SOTP) and has been adapted for use in programmes for people with learning disabilities. As Finkelhor's and Wolf's models are often seen as being complementary to each other, they are often combined in treatment approaches.

The good lives model

(Ward & Brown, 2004)

This model is described by Ward & Brown as 'a strength-based approach' and is based on the idea that there are 'primary human goods' that all human beings strive for in order to have a sense of purpose and meaning to their lives. A 'primary good' is defined as actions, states of affairs, characteristics, experiences and states of mind that are intrinsically beneficial to human beings, eg. friendship, intimacy, mastery experiences (being good at things), knowledge, health and meaningful work. Offending behaviour occurs when there is a problem with the way an individual seeks to achieve a 'primary good', for example turning to children in an attempt to meet the 'primary good' of intimacy and relationships.

Assessment issues

A thorough assessment is vital when trying to understand an individual's sexually offensive behaviours. Without a detailed assessment, it is difficult to ensure that an offender receives the appropriate treatment aimed at their specific needs. Clinical assessment of sexual offending should be based on clinical interview and psychometric assessment, in addition to the gathering of case details based on reports from multiple sources (eg. family, probation, police etc). Risk of reoffending also needs to be addressed within the assessment and, again, a number of formal risk assessments have been developed to assist in the accurate assessment of risk, such as SVR-20, STATIC-99 and SONAR.

Areas that are routinely covered in assessment are outlined below.

- **Personal history.** What experiences has the individual had that may predispose them to sexual offending? What current factors contribute to the cycle of offending? Are there personality factors that have made the individual vulnerable to offending? Is the individual willing to engage in treatment for their offending behaviour?

- **Family history.** Is there a history of criminal activity and antisocial behaviour within the family? Is there marital disharmony? Have family members misused alcohol and drugs? Is there a history of sexual abuse within the family? Although not a necessary precondition for offending, a higher rate of sexual abuse in childhood has been found in men with learning disabilities who sexually offend (Lindsay *et al*, 2001).

- **School history.** Was the individual socially isolated at school? Did they have an appropriate peer group or did they socialise with younger children to reduce feelings of isolation? Did they engage in delinquent behaviour at school, necessitating professional involvement at an early age?

- **Sexual history.** What is the range and extent of the individual's sexual experience? What is their primary sexual orientation? Do they regularly use pornography? What type of sexual fantasies do they engage in? Have they had any unusual sexual experiences? Have they been able to establish and maintain intimate and sexually satisfying relationships?

- **Occupational/social/leisure.** Does the individual have a range of meaningful occupational and recreational activities to engage in or are they understimulated and bored?
- **Drug and alcohol history.** Does the individual have a history of misusing drugs or alcohol? Both can be seen as disinhibitors that increase the risk of sexually offending.
- **Offending history.** Have there been previous sexual and non-sexual offences? What was the individual's lifestyle like around the time of these offences?

Psychometric assessment involves the administration of measures that have been adapted for use with men with learning disabilities. The Questionnaire on Attitudes Consistent with Sex Offences (QACSO) (Lindsay *et al,* 2006) assesses the degree to which an individual holds attitudes and beliefs that support sexual offending (eg. 'It is only women who wear tight clothes who can be raped'). The Victim Empathy Scale (Beckett & Fisher, 1994) looks at whether an individual takes full responsibility for their offending and acknowledges the full extent of the harm their behaviour could cause (eg. 'Do you think the victim enjoyed what happened?'). As it is also important to have an understanding of the individual's level of sexual knowledge and the degree to which they hold pro-social sexual attitudes, assessments such as the Socio-Sexual Knowledge and Attitudes Test (SSKAT) (Wish *et al*, 1980) and the Sexual Attitudes & Knowledge Assessment (SAK) are frequently used. Assessment tools such as these should only be used after appropriate training and under the supervision of an experienced clinician.

Treatment

For many years, community and inpatient services working with men with learning disabilities who have sexually offended or are at risk of sexually offending have had limited treatment options available to them. Historically, close supervision and pharmacological intervention have provided the most common treatment approaches. More recently, behavioural approaches aimed at addressing deviant sexual arousal and the provision of sex education and social skills have gradually became important components of psychological treatment packages. However, as a result of the advances made in the treatment of mainstream sex offenders, significant developments are underway, exploring and designing treatment approaches for men with learning disabilities.

Sex Offender Treatment Programmes (SOTP) have been available in prison settings for some time. However, it is only more recently that the Adapted Sex Offender Treatment Programme (ASOTP) has been available for prisoners whose IQ ranges from 65-80. Despite this, prisoners with learning disabilities are often excluded from the programme, whilst sex offenders with learning disabilities in hospital or in the community have had little access to such specialist treatment. Over the past 10 years, however, community and inpatient learning disability health services have been delivering and evaluating group treatment programmes for men with learning disabilities. In Scotland, Lindsay and colleagues (Lindsay *et al*, 1998; Lindsay 2004; 2005) have published a number of research papers focusing on the treatment of men in the community. Both community and inpatient treatment has been included in the programmes and research has been carried out by the UK Sex Offender

Treatment Services Collaborative – Learning Disabilities (SOTSEC-LD) (Sinclair *et al*, 2002). The treatment groups are based on and adapted from the prison SOTP and, as such, use a cognitive behavioural model of therapy in addition to psycho-educational components covering the following issues:

- victim empathy
- cognitive distortions
- sex education
- fantasy and sexual preference
- legal and illegal behaviours
- self-esteem
- social skills/relationships
- relapse prevention.

These programmes offer weekly or twice-weekly group treatment sessions and are commonly facilitated by a multidisciplinary group of professionals who have received training and ongoing supervision.

In addition to this specialist sex offender work, because many offenders are cared for and supervised in residential or inpatient settings, direct care staff play a crucial role in the ongoing monitoring that is essential in providing dynamic risk management. Monitoring the presence or absence of risk factors can only be carried out effectively by those staff who are aware of the risk profile for each individual and who are aware of their own role in ongoing assessment, risk management and longer-term treatment goals.

A key contribution to ongoing monitoring and risk assessment is the observation of service users in a variety of settings, situations and relationships, for example:

- behaviour in the community (eg. towards children, towards women, accessing community when children on way to or from school)

- relationships with staff (eg. over-familiar, asking personal questions, physical contact, acquiring personal information through other staff)

- interest in child-orientated materials (eg. TV programmes, photographs in magazines/newspapers, buying toys)

- relationships with other service users (eg. buying presents, giving money, bullying, following to toilets)

- use of internet.

In addition to these behavioural observations, there are a number of factors that have been linked to an increased risk of reoffending and that require ongoing monitoring, such as:

- intimacy deficits: relationship difficulties with girlfriend or boyfriend

- social influences: withdrawing from friends and family; spending more time with people who might be considered a negative influence
- attitudes: expressing views that condone sexual offending
- emotional/sexual self-regulation: using sex as a method of coping with negative emotions (eg. masturbating more, talking more about sex, more frequent use of pornography).

It is important that appropriate systems of monitoring and recording are in place and that all staff are aware of the types of behaviours or changes to look out for. If risk factors are noticed by staff, it is important they know who to pass this information on to, whether this is a senior member of the care team or an external professional such as a social worker. This will allow for the necessary risk management strategies to be put in place, whilst also ensuring the clinical team can meet the treatment needs of individuals. There may be times when changes in presentation or behaviour are not recognised, not communicated or not acted on in a way that addresses both safety and treatment goals.

The following case example describes the observations made by staff working with Mr B and the concerns they have in terms of potential risk.

Case example: Mr B

Mr B has a history of sexual abusive behaviour towards children and he himself is a victim of sexual abuse by family members and friends of the family. He presents a risk to others and is also vulnerable himself, as he sometimes finds it difficult to maintain appropriate boundaries with other services users who may attempt to engage in socially and sexually inappropriate behaviour. Whilst attending the day centre, Mr B is observed to respond to the flirtatious behaviour of another service user by tickling, engaging in banter and making sexually inappropriate gestures. Staff at the day centre have observed this behaviour and are concerned about the potential for this behaviour to progress. They are aware that both service users have access to the toilets during break time. They have concerns about Mr B's capacity to consent and are aware of the history of sexual offending behaviour of both service users.

Table 4A.2 illustrates two alternative approaches services may take, should they decide to respond to the risk they have observed regarding Mr B. The pros and cons of each of these approaches are highlighted.

Table 4A.2: Case example, Mr B

Service 1		**Service 2**	
The day centre staff decide they need to make sure that close supervision is maintained in order to ensure the risk is adequately managed. Mr B is unaware of this decision and receives no feedback about his behaviour.		The day centre staff communicate their concerns about Mr B to his keyworker, who raises them at a team meeting. The team suggests an increase in supervision at break time, in addition to individual work with Mr B to look at issues around boundaries and how to stay safe. Mr B agrees to do this with the keyworker. Over five sessions, they work together to explore his relationship with the other service user and the difference between friendships and relationships in terms of appropriate interactions and behaviour. They put together some guidelines about how Mr B might change his behaviour in order to ensure that he maintains boundaries and gives a clear message to the other service user. The keyworker asks Mr B for permission to contact the day centre to feed back about the work. He also asks for some feedback in order to establish whether Mr B has been able to implement the strategies or whether he requires more direct support.	
Pros	**Cons**	**Pros**	**Cons**
Appropriate identification of risky situation, which they then act upon. Prevents this specific situation from escalating. Manages the risk.	Does not allow Mr B to develop strategies to manage the risk. Does not allow Mr B the opportunity to learn about boundaries. Does not promote Mr B as someone responsible for his own safety; promotes Mr B's dependency on others.	Appropriate identification of risky situation, which they then act upon. Put in place risk management strategy whilst also addressing longer term treatment needs. Supports Mr B in developing understanding about boundaries and relationships, which may benefit him in other situations. Working collaboratively with Mr B may help him develop a sense of responsibility for his own behaviour.	Requires time and therefore resources, not only to provide one-to-one sessions but also to ensure that appropriate supervision and support are provided.

Table 4A.2: Case example, Mr B			
Service 1		**Service 2**	
Pros	**Cons**	**Pros**	**Cons**
		Working on the issues in a non-judgemental or punitive way allows for an open dialogue, which is likely to contribute to a positive therapeutic alliance between keyworker and Mr B. This may increase the possibility that Mr B will communicate future concerns regarding risk. Asking for feedback from the day centre ensures evaluation of intervention	

Pharmacological intervention

The use of medication in the treatment of sex offenders remains an area of controversy. Most commonly used in Europe and America are two hormonal medications that aim to reduce sexual drive, Cyproterone Acetate (CPA) and Medroxyprogesterone Acetate (MPA). Monitoring and evaluating the effectiveness of pharmacological interventions is fraught with difficulties, due to the combination of intrusive medical and physiological assessments required (eg. blood tests and penile plethysmography (PPG)), as well as psychophysiological assessments reliant on self-report (eg. frequency of masturbation, sexual tension and sexual fantasy), which may be unreliable. Furthermore, there are reports of high rates of withdrawal from pharmacological treatment due to the significant side effects, eg. developing breasts (Gordon & Grubin, 2004). More recently, selective serotonin reuptake inhibitors (SSRIs) have been considered as pharmacological treatment options for sex offenders. SSRIs may be of benefit by addressing obsessive-compulsive behaviour (eg. sexual ruminations and sexual urges) and producing a decrease in anxiety and impulsivity, and elevation in mood, with fewer side effects than CPA and MPA. However, the role of SSRIs in recidivism has not yet been established.

The use of pharmacological intervention should only be considered when psychological therapies are in place and where careful monitoring can be incorporated into the ongoing monitoring process. It is also essential for the clinical team to give considerable thought to the ethical concerns, such as consent to treatment, when working with sex offenders with learning disabilities.

Service issues

Working with people with learning disabilities who sexually offend can be challenging for services, as they face a combination of complex issues. Addressing the rights of people with learning disabilities to have sexual relationships, coping with issues of vulnerability, and managing the risk to staff and the public, for example, is a complicated balancing act in a society that has not come to terms with many of these issues. It is essential, therefore, that community and inpatient services develop policies regarding relationships and sexuality and provide ongoing training for care staff. Furthermore, the nature of sexual offending behaviour has significant implications for therapeutic relationships between staff and service user. Supervision and support are essential in ensuring that appropriate boundaries are maintained to provide a non-judgemental and non-punitive approach, whilst recognising and managing the ongoing risk issues.

Conclusion

For professionals in the field of forensic learning disabilities, working with individuals who have committed sexual offences or engaged in sexually inappropriate behaviour is not uncommon. Despite this, it is only recently that there have been significant developments in our understanding of this behaviour and the associated assessment and treatment issues. Risk management plans and psychosocial interventions must meet the needs of the individual whilst managing the risk to the public. Achieving this balance in addition to coping with the personal challenges experienced by those working closely with this population requires good teamwork, incorporating adequate training and supervision. Although still small, the growing evidence base is now providing literature on the assessment, treatment and management of sexual offenders with learning disabilities, which should be used to inform service development and practice.

References

Beckett R & Fisher D (1994) Victim Empathy Measure. In: R Beckett, A Beech, D Fisher and AS Fordham (Eds) *Community-based Treatment for Sex Offenders: An evaluation of seven treatment programmes* (pp136-40). London: Home Office.

Brown H & Turk V (1992) Defining sexual abuse as it affects adults with learning difficulties. *Mental Handicap* **20** 44-55.

Craft A (1993) The Moral Map. In: J Churchill J, A Craft, A Holding and C Horrocks (Eds) *It Could Never Happen Here: The prevention and treatment of sexual abuse of adults with learning disabilities in residential settings*. Nottingham: National Association for the Protection from Sexual Abuse of Adults and Children with Learning Disabilities.

Finkelhor D (1984) *Child Sexual Abuse: New theory and research*. New York: Free Press.

Finkelhor D (1986) *A Sourcebook on Child Sexual Abuse.* Beverley Hills, CA: Sage Publications.

Finkelhor D (1994) The international epidemiology of child sexual abuse. *Child Abuse and Neglect* **18** 409-417.

Gordon H & Grubin D (2004) Psychiatric aspects of the assessment and treatment of sex offenders. *Advances in Psychiatric Treatment* **10** 73-80.

Gross G (1985) *Activities of a Development Disabilities Adult Offender Project*. Olympia, WA: Washington State Developmental Disabilities Planning Council.

Hayes S (1991) Sex offenders. *Australia and New Zealand Journal of Developmental Disabilities* **17** 220-227.

Hayes S (2007) Women with learning disabilities who offend: what do we know? *British Journal of Learning Disabilities* **35** 187-191.

Hingsburger D, Griffiths D & Quinsey V (1991) Detecting counterfeit deviance: differentiating sexual deviance from sexual inappropriateness. *Habilitation Mental Health Care Newsletter* **10** 51-54.

Lindsay WR (2004) Sex offenders: conceptualisation of the issues, services, treatment and management. In: WR Lindsay, JL Taylor and P Sturmey (Eds) *Offenders with Developmental Disabilities*. Chichester: Wiley.

Lindsay WR (2005) Model underpinning treatment for sex offenders with mild intellectual disability: current theories of sex offending. *Mental Retardation* **43** 428-41.

Lindsay WR, Law J, Quinn K, Smart N & Smith AHW (2001) A comparison of physical and sexual abuse histories: sexual and non-sexual offenders with intellectual disability. *Child Abuse and Neglect* **25** 989-995.

Lindsay WR, Michie AM, Whitefield E, Victoria M, Grieve A & Carson D (2006) Response patterns on the Questionnaire Attitudes Consistent with Sex Offending in groups of sex offenders with intellectual disabilities. *Journal of Applied Research in Intellectual Disabilities* **19** (1) 47-53.

Lindsay WR, Neilson C, Morrison F & Smith A (1998) The treatment of six men with a learning disability convicted of sex offences with children. *British Journal of Clinical Psychology* **37** 83-98.

Luiselli JK (2000) Presentation of paraphilias and paraphilia related disorders in young adults with mental retardation: two case studies. *Mental Health Aspects of Developmental Disabilities* **3** 42-46.

Lund J (1990) Mentally retarded criminal offenders in Denmark. *British Journal of Psychiatry* **156** 726-731.

Lunsky Y, Frijters DM, Griffiths SL & Williston S (2007) Sexual knowledge and attitudes of men with intellectual disability who sexually offend. *Journal of Intellectual & Developmental Disability* **32** 74–81.

McCabe MP, Cummins RA & Reid SB (1994) An empirical study of the sexual abuse of people with intellectual disabilities. *Sexuality and Disability* **12** 297-306.

McCarthy M & Thompson D (1994) *Sex and Staff Training: A training manual for staff working with people with learning difficulties*. Brighton: Pavilion Publishing (Brighton) Ltd.

Murphy G (2007) Intellectual disability, sexual abuse, and sexual offending. In: A Carr, G O'Reilly, P Noonan Walsh and J Mcevoy (Eds) *The Handbook of Intellectual Disabilities and Clinical Psychology Practice*. London: Routledge.

Sinclair N, Booth SJ & Murphy G (2002) *Cognitive Behavioural Treatment for Men with Intellectual Disabilities Who Are at Risk of Sexual Offending*. Tizard Centre, University of Kent.

Ward T & Brown M (2004) The good lives model and conceptual issues in offender rehabilitation. *Psychology, Crime & Law* **10** 243-257.

Wish JR, McCombs KF & Edmonson B (1980) *The Socio-sexual Knowledge and Attitudes Test*. Wood Dale, IL: Stoeling.

Wolf SC (1988) A model of sexual aggression/addiction. (Special issues: the sexually unusual: guide to understanding and helping). *Journal of Social Work and Human Sexuality* **7** 131-148.

Section 4

Part B

Working with firesetters with learning disabilities

Eddie Chaplin

History and background

The literature reports a long association between people with learning disabilities and firesetting, stretching over centuries. Early attempts to explain this phenomenon in terms of mental disorder were previously seen as trying to absolve the offender of their wrongdoing by arguing that they were not in total control of their actions. This went against the concept of free will, which was at the foundation of the criminal justice system of the time. Early theories examining pathological firesetting associated it with pubescent, mentally retarded girls with menstrual and psychosexual difficulties. By the 1850s, the debate was considering whether individuals with a range of mental disorder may engage in firesetting or, alternatively, whether this was an indication of a specific mental disorder (ie. pyromania). (See Geller, 1992 for a more detailed history.) In spite of these early theories and debates, the roles of both learning disabilities and gender in firesetting remain unclear, with relatively few studies focusing on female firesetters (see Tennant *et al*, 1971 and Taylor *et al*, 2006).

What is arson?

The Ministry of Justice website (www.crimereduction.gov.uk/arson/arson2.htm) defines arson as the 'wilful or deliberate setting fire to another's house, car or similar property'. It is categorised as a property offence, which can be carried out as an intentional act and/or through recklessness. By incorporating recklessness, a jury is required to look beyond the motivations of the offender; as well as focusing on intent, it also has to consider whether the perpetrator was reckless in their actions and whether life was endangered as a result. When the offence endangers another's life, then it is defined as 'arson with intent'.

Arson is taken extremely seriously by the criminal justice system and as a result it carries a maximum penalty of a life sentence. Many observers perceive it to be punished more severely than some other crimes.

Despite a downward trend in the recorded figures of fires in the 10-year period 1995-2005 (Department for Communities and Local Government, 2007), arson remains the most common cause of fires; in some areas of the UK, arson has accounted for 82% of all fires (DCLG, 2007). Over the last decade, the number of malicious fires attended by the fire service has doubled and it now stands at 85,000 a year. Records show that, of a total of 869,400 calls made to the fire brigade in the UK in 2005, less then half were real fires and 439,100 were false alarms. Together, the significant number of malicious fires and high number of hoax calls increase the cost to the public in terms of risk of injury, death and property damage. It is not only a criminal offence to make hoax calls, but in many cases hoax calls are also part of an arsonist's repertoire of fire-related behaviours and offence profile.

In the UK, the estimated cost of dealing with fires was approximately £3.3 billion in 2003, with the total cost of fire to the country as high as £7.7 billion (Office of the Deputy Prime Minister, 2005). It is difficult to determine the full impact of fire, as fire statistics are kept in different agencies with different priorities, terminology and recording, particularly the various emergency services.

Firesetting and mental disorder

Within the ICD-10 and DSM-IV diagnostic manuals (American Psychiatric Association, 2000; World Health Organization, 1992), pyromania is the only diagnosis that refers specifically to firesetting. The term 'pyromania' was an early attempt to describe pathological firesetters. It is described as a disorder of impulse, characterised by setting more than one fire, an interest or fascination, pleasure gratification and a release of tension, not due to any other associated psychiatric disorder and not for monetary gain or for any of the other common motives for arson (such as crime concealment, political motives etc). Whether such a disorder exists is still a topic of debate, although it is a diagnosis that is little used in clinical practice.

Recidivism rates for arson are variable across populations, from 4% to 60% (Brett, 2004). Within learning disabilities populations, there may be an increased risk of engaging in alternative offending behaviour, particularly if fire is used as a way of coping or communicating, and where treatment approaches have failed to support the individual in developing alternative but equally effective ways of coping.

Prevalence

In short, no one knows the true size of the problem. Estimates have varied over the years, making it extremely difficult to interpret studies to give overall prevalence, given the different research settings and methodologies employed (eg. definition of learning disabilities, hospital or community samples, measures used etc). In Victoria State, Australia, Wallace *et al* (1998) examined a sample of convicted arsonists (*n*115, 106 male and 9 female) and found that 48 appeared on the psychiatric case register. Further examination of this sample found that only personality disorder and substance abuse were found to be significantly associated with arson. More specific to learning disabilities, Lewis & Yarnell (1951), using case studies, identified that 50% of 1,300 firesetters had learning disabilities, whilst Walker & McCabe (1973) found that individuals with learning disabilities in hospital accounted for a third of patients detained on hospital orders but were responsible for nearly 50% of arson offences.

More recently, Taylor *et al* (2002) reported findings from an unpublished thesis that 20% of a forensic learning disability hospital sample in the UK had convictions for arson.

Why do people set fires?

The 'only viable option' theory (Jackson *et al*, 1987) puts forward the idea that arson is used by the perpetrator to handle situations they find difficult to tolerate and/or manage. They may have tried other strategies that have failed, or may have found the situation too difficult or threatening even to try to resolve. Arson is therefore seen as a very effective way of coping with a range of difficulties, even if only in the short term. These situations can be:

- internal (in the form of unwanted thoughts and feelings)
- external (unwanted attention, bullying, relationship problems).

In this context, arson is seen as the means to an end. The inability to cope and address problems in a socially acceptable way is at the roots of the offending behaviour. These problems present significant difficulties for the individual, even though they may seem insignificant to others.

Jackson (1994) makes a distinction between pathological arsonists and non-pathological arsonists. Non-pathological arson can be characterised by people who set fires for a number of reasons, including peer pressure. This is often a single offence where the issue or motivation for the fire is resolved by the fire (eg. insurance, revenge, concealment, political statement). It can also be seen in some as a passing phase, where fires are set through play or experimentation. Pathological arson is associated with repeated firesetting that takes place in the context of a certain set of circumstances. The individual is likely to suffer from mental illness or personality problems and is most commonly alone when committing the offence. Jackson (1994) and Jackson *et al* (1987) examined the characteristics of pathological firesetters and listed five criteria:

1. recidivism
2. fires aimed at property rather than people
3. acting alone or repetitively with single accomplice
4. evidence of personality, psychiatric or emotional disturbance
5. absence of financial or political gain.

Although it is labelled a functional analysis model, Jackson's model is more than a purely behavioural approach in that it also hypothesises about the role of cognitions that maintain firesetting behaviours (Clare *et al*, 1992).

Two additional approaches used to examine the profile and behaviour of firesetters are:

- typologies
- characteristics.

Typologies

In a paper on firesetters, Prins *et al* (1985) outlined common reasons for setting fires, which he divided into distinct typologies such as revenge, financial gain, political motivation and pathological firesetting. However, not all typologies have a clear and specific motive. Prins made the distinction between pathological and non-pathological arsonists and purported a link between mental disorder, learning disabilities and firesetting. The focus on this association has weakened over the past decade, with a shift to identifying common individual characteristics.

Characteristics

This approach seeks to find commonalties – shared characteristics – in an attempt to build a profile of the firesetter. Shared characteristics include:

- poor education
- difficulties with employment
- from deprived area/background
- poor social skills
- problems with being assertive
- low self-esteem.

Are people with learning disabilities more likely to set fires?

For many years, researchers and clinicians seem to have been determined to establish whether or not there is an association between arson and people with learning disabilities. The debate continues with little evidence to support either side of the argument unequivocally. Nevertheless, as clinicians working with offenders with learning disabilities, we are likely to come across individuals who set fires. Despite there being insufficient evidence to support a clear association between learning disability and arson, research has been carried out to establish which of the characteristics often found in the profile of firesetters are also common in a learning disability population. It is possible that there are a number of factors that may predispose individuals with learning disabilities and mental disorder to set fires. Impairment in communication, poor emotion regulation, problem-solving skills and impulse control are examples of such factors. It is possible that an individual with learning disabilities may not be aware of the full consequences of their actions, and may not show intent or have an understanding of the danger of fire and fire-related behaviour. For example, a fascination for fire or a special interest in fire engines or uniforms may result in a range of fire-related behaviours, including arson and hoax calls, which can be indirectly dangerous to others.

It is generally accepted that, for the majority of people with learning disabilities, fire is not used for financial or political gain. Rather, Jackson *et al*'s model of the 'only viable option' (1987) provides a useful model, highlighting the role of arson as a maladaptive strategy to cope with a range of difficulties, which may also provide an effective method of communication.

Assessment and treatment

The functional analysis approach adopted by Jackson *et al* (1987) provides a useful framework for assessment, by creating a clear formulation of the general setting conditions, dispositional and situational antecedents, triggers, maintaining factors and consequences. For example, Jackson *et al* (1987) found that many people with learning disabilities who set fires were considered to be socially ineffective. The three most common reported antecedents were feeling angry, low social attention and feeling sad/depressed. As a consequence of the subsequent firesetting, individuals benefited in a number of ways, including gaining social attention, avoiding a situation or feeling powerful (Clare *et al*, 1992).

Carrying out a detailed functional analysis is time consuming, as it can often require detailed analysis of several fires. **Table 4B.1** outlines the information necessary to complete an analysis of each fire. (Examples of this approach are further illustrated in the case study later in this chapter.)

Stages of the assessment

Devise a timeline and history of offences using an ABC format (see **Table 4B.1**).

Table 4B.1: Using the ABC format to complete an analysis of a fire

Antecedents *What happened before?*	What were the setting conditions, dispositional and situational antecedents or specific triggers? Was there planning, was it impulsive, was it in the context of substance and/or alcohol misuse?
Behaviour *What occurred?* *How was the fire started?* *If there was a plan, how was it executed?*	How was it done – what materials were used (ie. accelerants, type of fuel)? Opportunity? Was it with peers or alone? Did the person stay and watch what happened or did they leave?
Consequences *What happened afterwards?*	Was there any demonstrable gain to the individual? Feelings of excitement or confidence, relief, reward, increase in self-esteem? Or was a planned goal achieved through the action?

The assessment process will also need to include information on:

- personal factors:
  - mental state before, during and afterwards
  - interpersonal issues
  - family history
  - social problems
  - psychiatric history

  - emotional and psychological problems e.g. emotion dysregulation, impulsivity, anxiety, fire fascination etc.
  - communication skills

- offending history:
  - general
  - other offending
  - previous firesetting
  - firesetting not having led to convictions
  - fire-related (including offences related to fire services such as hoax calls)

- medico-legal:
  - Did the person know the consequences of their actions?
  - What did the person understand would be the outcome of the fire (eg. damage, injury etc)?

The use of specific specialist instruments can help to provide a structure and framework for different parts of the assessment. Murphy (1990) developed two assessment tools:

- Fire Assessment Schedule (Murphy, 1990; Murphy & Clare, 1996): a structured interview based on 32 questions divided into two sections to examine cognitions pre- and post-fire

- Fire Interest Rating Scale (Murphy, 1990): 14 descriptions of fire-related situations rated from 'very exciting' and 'lovely/nice' to 'absolutely horrible' and 'most upsetting' along a seven-point scale.

Treatment

Currently, there is little evidence available regarding the treatment of firesetters. Descriptions of treatment approaches include a group programme for female firesetters (Taylor *et al*, 2006). This study showed that, despite a common offence (ie. arson), individuals within the group differed in terms of assessment and outcome results. The group is reported to have responded well to a cognitive behavioural approach. This study was a pilot, however, and although the authors advise caution in interpreting the results, those attending the treatment were able to engage satisfactorily with the programme. Taylor *et al* (2002) earlier reported on a mixed gender group of 14 firesetters within low secure services, which showed significant improvements on the fire-specific measures. There have also been examples (using individual case studies) using cognitive behavioural approaches (Clare *et al*, 1992), and a social skills programme for firesetters (Rice & Chaplin 1979). Both individual and group studies highlight the need for multifaceted, multidisciplinary approaches to treatment, including:

- education:
  - dangers of fire
  - fire prevention
  - fire safety

- skills development (looking at alternative methods of dealing with emotions, problem solving and assertiveness):
  - interpersonal
  - cognitive
  - behavioural
  - communication
- relapse prevention
- mental health (treating any underlying mental disorder)
- offence cycle (examining the individual's approach to offending in what might predispose, precipitate and maintain the offending behaviour):
  - experience of fire
  - loss for self and victims
  - reasons for firesetting
  - relationship between fire and emotion.

Case study: Rupert Holding

The following case study illustrates the principles underpinning the assessment and treatment of firesetters, and highlights the need for close multidisciplinary working.

Rupert Holding is a 22-year-old man who has mild learning disabilities. Rupert is currently being detained under Section 37/41 of the Mental Health Act (1983), following sentencing for arson with intent to endanger life. Rupert has no formal psychiatric history. He has a caution for setting a minor fire a couple of years ago. This and the index offence are his only known forensic history. The information on admission (and Rupert's initial explanations for setting fires) was that he was 'in with the wrong crowd' and that it was not his fault. He denies any intent but there is other evidence and there are suspicions. Police have found hoards of lighters in his bedsit and in his old bedroom at home. There have also been a number of unsolved fires in the local area. Rupert does not admit to sexual arousal or excitement when he sets fires, although he describes feeling relaxed when he watches fire. He denies that watching fires on TV affects him in any way, but it is observed that he appears excited whilst watching a series on fire-fighting. When approached about this he denied it, but continues to watch the programme in his own room rather than communal areas.

Assessment: The initial part of the assessment of Rupert involves creating a chronology to try and demonstrate his life history and events (see **Figure 4B.1**).

The dateline shown in **Figure 4B.1** provides a dynamic chronology, with more details added as they become available to help to generate a possible hypothesis.

Figure 4B.1: Dateline for Rupert Holding, Clematis Ward

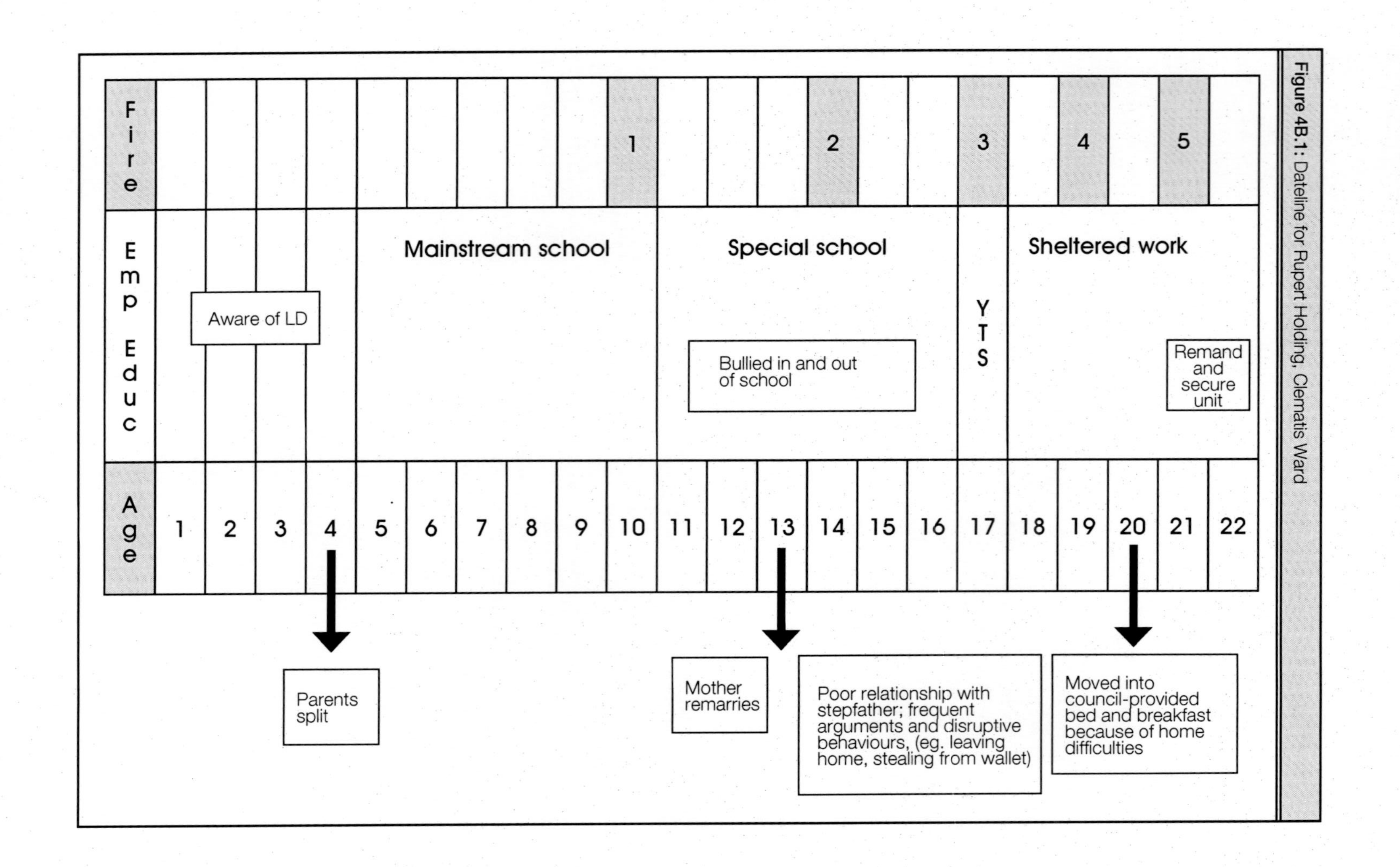

Figure 4B.2: Preliminary formulation for Rupert Holding

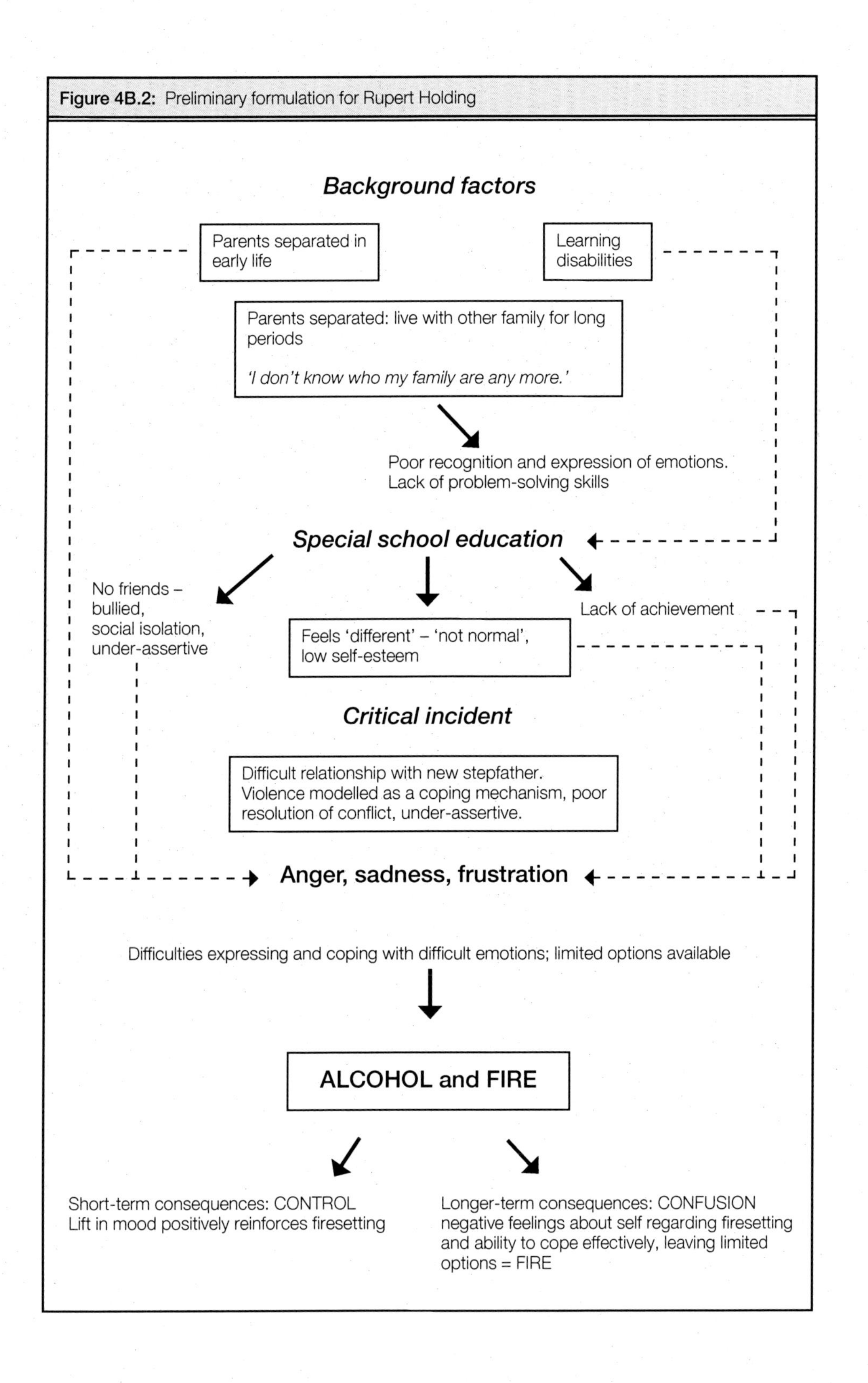

One of the first observations we can make is that Rupert's current account of events differs from his previously known forensic history. While exploring his history of firesetting, Rupert discloses three further fires. Each of the fires is examined using a functional analysis approach. Together with information gathered about his personal history, this allows for a preliminary formulation to be developed and shared with Rupert (see **Figure 4B.2**).

Treatment: Rupert is interested in the formulation and would like to learn more about why he sets fires; he believes that if he knew the reason he sets fires, this would help him to stop. The formulation also provides a framework intervention and treatment.

In the case of Rupert, the triggers included interpersonal conflict that was ineffectively dealt with due to lack of assertiveness, leading to difficult emotions such as anger, sadness and frustration. This led to alcohol use and firesetting, both of which provided only a short-term solution for Rupert in terms of lifting his mood. However, the long-term consequences further reinforced his negative feelings about himself and his inability to cope effectively, thereby increasing the likelihood of future firesetting as his only coping mechanism.

For the first two years of Rupert's admission, he takes part in the following individual and group sessions, in conjunction with an active day programme of occupation and leisure:

- assertiveness group
- coping with change group
- assessing risk of holding a lighter
- alcohol education
- offending cycle and relapse prevention
- coping with feelings group
- community reintegration
- pharmacology (depression)
- fire education.

These treatments are all related not only to firesetting behaviours but also to underlying mental disorder (depression, in Rupert's case) and other issues such as alcohol. Much of the treatment package is aimed at improving Rupert's emotion recognition, problem-solving and communication skills, producing positive feelings through alternative reactions to adverse events, and promoting recognition of risky situations.

Service considerations

In providing services for firesetters, a number of considerations need to be taken into account around safety, including the risk the individual poses to themselves and others within the service. There is no single way to approach this, and it is guided by the philosophy and culture within the clinical areas. As a result, the approach is not always consistent. Some services are risk averse with regard to certain procedures, whilst others take calculated risks. Risk management strategies in the past for firesetters have varied greatly, depending on the organisation and its culture. The following examples illustrate how different services may manage access to lights for cigarettes:

- prison: inmates allowed matches
- secure unit 1: lighters allowed during waking hours, signed in and out, with the ability to confiscate
- secure unit 2: matches and lighters allowed
- secure unit 3: device on a central wall for lighting cigarettes
- secure unit 4: only staff have lighters
- residential service 1: no smoking policy, therefore no lighters/matches allowed
- residential service 2: designated smoking area but staff hold lighters.

The ban on smoking in NHS areas may in some ways impact on the ability to systematically assess risk prior to discharge.

Conclusion

It would seem that, unfortunately, academic and research interest in arson in the field of learning disabilities has dwindled following its peak in the late 1980s and early 1990s. It is unclear why this might be the case but, as a result, there is currently little evidence regarding the treatment of this group and, significantly, its effectiveness in terms of longer-term recidivism. From the description of group and individual programmes, however, a functional analysis approach to assessment and treatment based on a cognitive-behavioural model provides us with the most useful framework. Whilst offence-specific work is important, treatment must inevitably address underlying issues such as emotion regulation and communication, as well as any underlying mental disorder, rather than focusing solely on risk management.

References

American Psychiatric Association (2000) *Diagnostic and Statistical Manual of Mental Disorders (DSM–IV)*. Washington, DC: American Psychiatric Association.

Brett A (2004) Kindling theory on arson. *Australian & New Zealand Journal of Psychiatry* **38** 419-425.

Clare ICH, Murphy GH, Cox D & Chaplin EH (1992) Assessment and treatment of fire setting: a single case investigation using a cognitive behavioural model. *Criminal Behaviour and Mental Health* **2** 253-268.

Department for Communities and Local Government (2007) *Fire Statistics, United Kingdom 2005*. London: Department for Communities and Local Government.

Geller JL (1992) Pathological firesetting in adults. *International Journal of Law and Psychiatry* **15** 282-302.

Jackson HF (1994) Assessment of fire-setters. In: M McMurran and J Hodge (Eds) *The Assessment of Criminal Behaviours in Secure Settings* (pp94-126). London: Jessica Kingsley.

Jackson HF, Glass C & Hope S (1987) A Functional Analysis of Recidivistic Arson. *British Journal of Clinical Psychology* **26** 175-185.

Lewis NDC & Yarnell H (1951) *Pathological Firesetting (Pyromania). (Nervous & Mental Disease Monograph No 82)*. New York: Coolidge Foundation.

Murphy G (1990) Analysis of motivation and fire-related interests in people with a mild learning difficulty who set fires. Paper presented at the International Congress on Treatment of Mental Illness and Behavioural Disorders in Mentally Retarded People, Amsterdam. Cited in: ICH Clare, GH Murphy, D Cox and EH Chaplin (1992) Assessment and treatment of fire setting: A single case investigation using a cognitive behavioural model. *Criminal Behaviour and Mental Health* **2** 253-268.

Murphy GH & Clare ICH (1996) Analysis of motivation in people with mild learning disabilities (mental handicap) who set fires. *Psychology Crime and Law* **2** 153-164.

Office of the Deputy Prime Minister (2005) *The Economic Cost of Fire: Estimates for 2003*. London: ODPM.

Prins H, Tennant G & Trick K (1985) Motives for arson (fireraising). *Medicine, Science and the Law* **25** 275-278.

Rice ME & Chaplin TC (1979) Social skills training for hospitalised male arsonists. *Journal of Behaviour Therapy and Experimental Psychiatry* **10** 105-108.

Taylor JL, Robertson A, Thorne I, Belshaw T & Watson A (2006) Responses of female fire-setters with mild and borderline intellectual disabilities to a group intervention. *Journal of Applied Research in Intellectual Disabilities* **19** (2) 179-190.

Taylor JL, Thorne I, Robertson A & Avery G (2002) Evaluation of a group intervention for convicted arsonists with mild and borderline intellectual disabilities. *Criminal Behaviour and Mental Health* **12** 282-293.

Tennant TJ, McQuaid A, Loughnane T & Hands AJ (1971) Female arsonists. *British Journal of Psychiatry* **119** 497-502.

Walker N & McCabe S (1973) *Crime and Insanity in England*. Edinburgh: University Press.

Wallace C, Mullen P, Burgess P, Palmer S, Ruschena D & Browne C (1998) Serious criminal offending and mental disorder. Case linkage study. *British Journal of Psychiatry* **172** 477-484.

World Health Organization (1992) *The ICD-10 International Classification of Mental and Behavioural Disorders*. Geneva: World Health Organization.

Section 4

Part C

Working with violent offenders with learning disabilities

Max Pickard, Jayne Henry and Donna Yates

Introduction

The study of violence by people with learning disabilities is fraught with difficulties. Studies investigating the prevalence and nature of violence in people with learning disabilities tend to consider the umbrella term 'challenging behaviour', but there has been scant research specifically on violent offending within this population. Conceptually, the terms 'violence' and 'challenging behaviour' are blurred and overlap with each other. However, it can be useful to draw a distinction between the high frequency, low impact aggression that is characteristic of 'challenging behaviour' and the lower frequency, higher impact aggression that is characteristic of 'violence' classified as offending. This chapter will discuss the issues related to violence (low frequency, high impact aggression) and its treatment and management in clinical practice.

Background

The incidence of violence by people with learning disabilities is not clear. Taylor (2002), reviewing the evidence, cites figures of between 20% and 60% for the prevalence of aggression in people with learning disabilities across community and inpatient settings. The variance in figures is almost certainly due to varying sample populations and differing definitions of violence and aggression used across studies. With particular regard to offending, Hogue *et al* (2006) report a lifetime incidence of violent offences of 17% in people with learning disabilities in the community, from a sample of people who had been in an open hospital unit or attending an attached day service.

Violent offending behaviour

Offenders with a history of violence who present to services may previously have been dealt with by the criminal justice system and/or be diverted to health services as a result of offences such as grievous bodily harm (GBH), actual bodily harm (ABH) and aggravated burglary. It is also likely, as a result of the issues relating to the reporting and prosecution of crimes by people with learning disabilities, that there will be no resulting conviction, even where there has been a significant history of violence and aggression.

There is little descriptive data outlining the type of violent offending most commonly found in the learning disabled population. However, based on clinical experience, although people with learning disabilities can be more impulsive in their reactions to given situations, which can lead to violence, this does not rule out the occurrence of serious and dangerous pre-planned violence.

Assessment

Clinicians working with violent offenders are under pressure to predict and appropriately manage the risk of violence. However, effective risk management requires clinicians to look beyond specific risk behaviour to develop an understanding of the factors leading to violent behaviour.

In the general population, the single best predictor of future violence is previous violence, and there is no reason to suspect this is any different in the learning disabled population. Whilst an understanding of the factors leading to the development and maintenance of violent behaviour is important in terms of intervention, all staff working with offenders with a history of violence need to be familiar not only with the details of the index offence but also with previous violent behaviour, for which there may or may not have been any convictions. This will provide additional information to guide intervention strategies and will also form an important basis for risk management plans. **Figure 4C.1** shows the information that should be included in an assessment of violence.

The information should be gathered and corroborated wherever possible from a range of sources, including:

- self-report
- clinical interview
- archival data
- multi-agency reports
- police records
- family interview
- depositions and witness statements from the trial.

It can be helpful to conceptualise violence in terms of factors that drive or predispose violent behaviour and factors that inhibit or reduce violent behaviour. The drive (or motivation) to violence can be instrumental (in order to achieve a specific goal, such as theft or escape) or reactive (driven by anger, emotional states, or sadism), or often a combination of both. Considering these factors can help in assessing and managing the risk of violence and guiding treatment approaches.

Figure 4C.1: Information required for assessment of violence

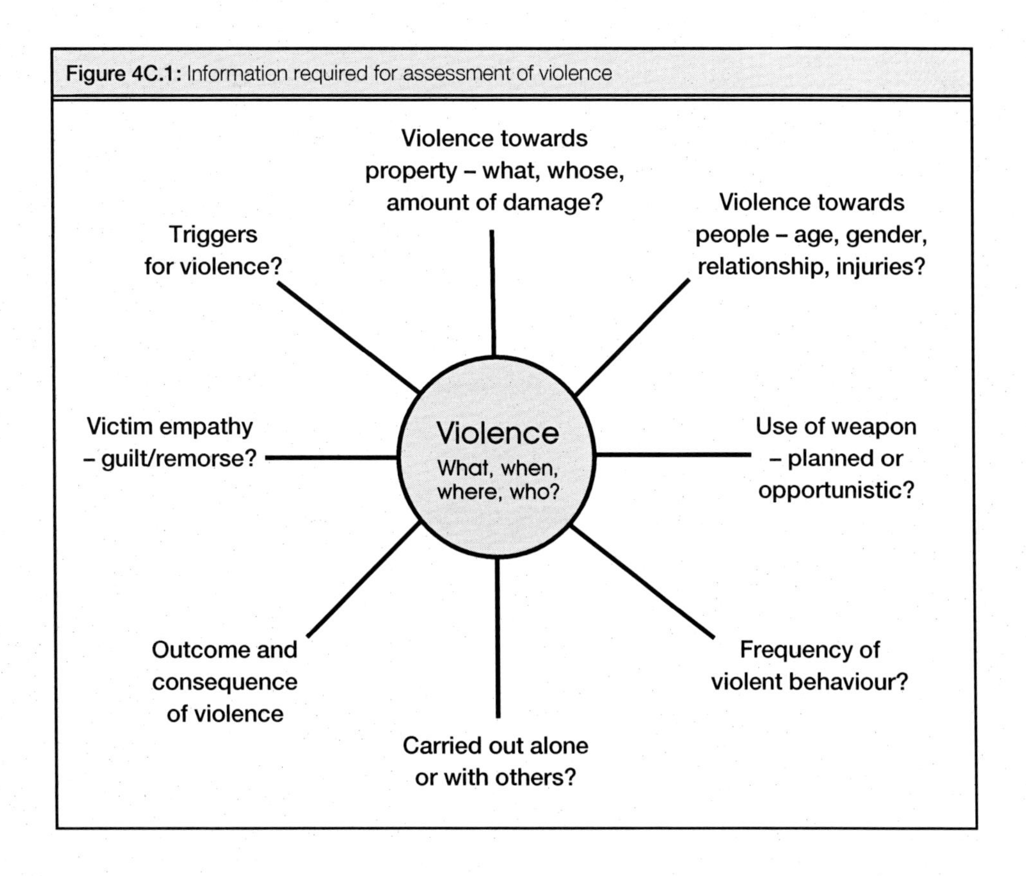

Once a detailed account of the nature of previous violence has been obtained, an exploration of the underlying factors that have contributed to the onset and maintenance of the behaviour should be carried out in order to be able to develop an individual formulation. Some of the key factors that have been found to be associated with violence, or that may play a significant part in the manifestation of violent behaviour and should therefore be included in an assessment are:

- substance misuse
- personality disorder
- mental illness
- neurodevelopmental disorder
- organic dysfunction
- assessment measures.

Substance misuse

This is strongly associated with violence in the general population and, whilst studies are lacking in the learning disabled population, there is no reason to think that this correlation does not apply. Substance misuse is often funded through criminal activities and hence violence may be instrumental to obtain funds (eg. robbery). The process of deinstitutionalisation has resulted in greater opportunity and access to drugs and alcohol for people with learning disabilities. Many substances cause disinhibition (most notably, alcohol) and/or act as stimulants (such as amphetamines and cocaine), which may raise the risk of violence. Some substances may cause or predispose to psychotic or affective symptoms of mental illness.

Personality disorder

By definition, antisocial personality disorder and psychopathy include behaviours such as impulsivity, irritability, aggressive behaviour, law breaking and lack of remorse. A combination of neurobiological and psycho-social factors such as family environment, witnessing domestic violence, history of physical abuse and low self-esteem are relevant risk factors for the development of antisocial personality disorder and psychopathy and increased risk of violence.

Mental illness (ie. psychosis and mood disorder)

- *Psychotic symptoms* (such as occur in schizophrenia, for example) can have a powerful effect on violence. Paranoid delusions may drive violence as a result of increased fear and arousal, and may give the individual a perfectly valid reason (in their mind) to act violently in the name of self-protection. Command hallucinations may instruct an individual to act violently, although the relationship between command hallucinations and violence is not well defined and must be taken with some caution in the learning disabled population.

- *Affective symptoms* are also important to consider. The relationship between violence and depression is not clear. Mania often results in disinhibition, which erodes a protective factor. Irritability can also occur with mania, and is clearly an important factor.

(See **Section 3A: Mental illness, learning disabilities and offending** for an overview of mental disorder and offending.)

Neurodevelopmental disorder

This covers autistic spectrum disorder (ASD) and attention deficit and hyperactivity disorder (ADHD). There are a number of difficulties experienced by people with ASD that may be associated with an increased risk of violence:

- impairment of empathy (empathy is a powerful inhibitor of aggression, and conversely its absence removes this protective factor)

- increased anxiety and frustration, particularly if rituals cannot be completed or routine is disrupted

- ritualistic behaviours may be misinterpreted by others as threatening or provocative (eg. invading another person's body space may provoke an aggressive response)

- areas of special interest may include violence, weapons or martial arts.

- impulsive, reckless and thrill-seeking behaviours commonly seen in adults with ADHD, and often further exacerbated by a higher rates of substance misuse and antisocial personality disorder.

(See **Section 3B: Neurodevelopmental disorders and offending** for a more comprehensive overview of offending in this group.)

Organic dysfunction (ie. head injury, epilepsy, dysexecutive syndrome)

- **Dysexecutive syndrome:** a condition where higher brain functions (such as judgement, pre-planning and the ability to inhibit behaviour) is impaired. It is normally associated with damage or dysfunction of the frontal lobes of the brain resulting in impulsive behaviour with little consideration of the consequences. Conversely, the lack of ability to pre-plan means that planned assaults or violence are extremely unlikely.

- **Ictal states:** epilepsy may, rarely, predispose to violence. The association is unclear but probably uncommon. Very rarely, violence can occur whilst having a seizure, classically due to a seizure occurring in the temporal lobe, or possibly frontal lobe of the brain. This can occur without the normal obvious signs of epilepsy, such as shaking or jerking. However, there will normally be an alteration of level of consciousness.

Assessment measures

The assessment of anger control and aggression is of particular relevance to the assessment of violent offenders. The Novaco Anger Scale and Provocation Inventory (NAS-PI) (Novaco, 1994a) has been used both clinically and in research for offenders with learning disabilities. The NAS uses self-ratings to assess cognitive, arousal and behavioural aspects of anger in addition to regulation skills, whilst the PI explores reactions to a range of anger-provoking situations. Taylor & Novaco (2004) have explored the impact of modifications to the measure on the reliability and validity of the scale for offenders with learning disabilities, and found satisfactory results. In addition, the Ward Anger Rating Scale (WARS) (Novaco, 1994b) provides an assessment tool based on informant ratings, which gives an indication of affective-behavioural anger attributes based on a seven-day observation period for inpatient settings. To examine the severity of incidents, there are measures such as the Modified Overt Aggression Scale (MOAS) (Kay *et al*, 1988), which give an average score across four types of incident: physical aggression, verbal aggression, auto aggression (against self) and aggression against property. Each of the categories are weighted and scored from 0 (did not occur) to increasing severity from 1 to 4.

Treatment

Bearing in mind the likelihood of multiple factors relating to the development of violent behaviours and the complex presentation of violent offenders, it is unlikely that effective treatment can be delivered by a single treatment approach. Furthermore, the presence of comorbid mental disorder such as substance misuse, personality disorder or ADHD will impact significantly on engagement and motivation. It is surprising, therefore, that in clinical settings it is not uncommon for people with learning disabilities who have a history of aggression and violence to receive treatment based primarily on anger management and/or pharmacology.

Anger management/treatment

Anger management is often provided by community and inpatient services for people with learning disabilities who present with verbally and physically aggressive behaviour. Programmes designed by Benson (1994) and O'Neill *et al* (1997) will be familiar to those working in the challenging behaviour field.

There has been growing interest in the development of treatment approaches for people with learning disabilities who have a history of violent offending (Allan *et al*, 2001; Lindsay *et al*, 2003; Taylor *et al*, 2002). Taylor *et al*'s pilot study (2002) and the subsequent randomised control trial (Taylor *et al*, 2005) describes the move from group to individual CBT treatment for offenders with learning disabilities who have a history of serious aggression and violence. Key ingredients of the manualised treatment package are spread across a two-stage approach:

1. Preparatory phase: six sessions using a psycho-educational approach aimed at overcoming motivational and engagement issues.

2. Treatment phase: 12 sessions incorporating a range of CBT techniques aimed at improving self-monitoring skills, improving self-control and cognitive restructuring (learning to recognise, challenge and change unhelpful thoughts and attitudes that contribute to the maintenance of anger and violence).

The treatment is delivered by a therapist trained in CBT, in collaboration with the keyworker. As yet this has only been provided within inpatient settings but with some promising results.

Offender treatment programmes for people without learning disabilities has shifted from a focus on anger management/treatment as a stand-alone treatment package, to just one part of a multifactorial programme. The complex needs of violent offenders with learning disabilities requires an individualised and multifaceted treatment approach that looks beyond anger issues. This should include multidisciplinary treatment goals that aim to address underlying issues that may contribute to the maintenance of violent behaviour such as (Bishop & Henry 2008):

- low self-esteem
- communication difficulties
- assertiveness
- emotional awareness and regulation
- relationships
- anxiety
- substance misuse.

Pharmacological treatment

Violence is not a medical illness and it is therefore not surprising that there is no licensed long-term pharmacological treatment. Despite this, it is possible to see a reduction in violence as a result of pharmacological treatment when this has been able to address an underlying mental illness, epilepsy and other neurodevelopmental disorders such as ADHD. Where there is no mental disorder, caution should be used when considering pharmacological intervention for violent behaviour. The results from Tyrer *et al*'s (2008) randomised control trial question the use of antipsychotics in the use of controlling violence in people with learning disabilities (see **Section 3A: Mental illness, learning disabilities and offending** for further discussion). In spite of this, the most common medications used are as follows.

Benzodiazepines (eg. diazepam, lorazepam): benzodiazepines act on specific receptors in the brain (benzodiazepine receptors) and induce a feeling of calmness, sedation and tranquillity. Whilst they are very effective agents, they are addictive and tolerance to these effects soon occurs. Occasionally, individuals can become quite disinhibited on benzodiazepines in what is known as 'paradoxical disinhibition'. If this occurs, then violence may worsen, and future benzodiazepine use must be avoided. Benzodiazepines are often used, effectively, as emergency sedation. However, the problems of addiction and tolerance mean their use as regular medication (even in the short term) must be done with great caution, and care must be taken that they are not used excessively or too regularly as emergency or 'as required' medication.

'Typical' antipsychotics (eg. chlorpromazine, haloperidol): typical antipsychotics have a powerful effect on many receptors in the brain, especially dopamine. The various classes and types of typical antipsychotics vary in how strongly they act on various receptors and hence how significant their side effects are. However, they all usually cause some degree of sedation, which can be helpful. It is possible that they may also exert an action on inhibiting violence through other mechanisms, although this is speculative. Typical antipsychotics tend to be used both in the short term as regular medication and as emergency sedation. They have a significant side effect profile and can cause excess sedation.

'Atypical' antipsychotics (eg. olanzapine, risperidone): atypical antipsychotics function in much the same way as their 'typical' cousins, but they are far more specific in action, selectively blocking dopamine transmission in the brain. Some have a sedative effect that is usually milder than the typical antipsychotics. Atypical antipsychotics are usually used in much the same way as typical antipsychotics but have a better side effect profile. They cause less sedation, which is often an advantage unless this is specifically needed.

Other pharmacological agents: some antiepileptic drugs, such as carbamazepine or sodium valproate, alongside drugs such as lithium, are used as mood stabilisers for bipolar affective disorder. There is some evidence suggestive that these drugs can lower impulsivity or mood variation in the general population, and occasionally these drugs are used in people with learning disabilities for these problems. However, they are not licensed for this use, and there is no convincing evidence that they are helpful.

Working with violence

Care organisations have an obligation to their staff and service users to provide training in the prevention and management of violence. There is a plethora of information on this subject, including from the National Institute for Clinical Excellence (2005) and Royal College of Psychiatrists (1998; 2005), as well as BILD's physical intervention guidelines for people with learning disabilities (Harris *et al*, 1996; 2008). The BILD guidance is particularly useful when in adopting a person-centred approach.

Working with service users who can threaten or present violently can be a challenging and stressful experience. Violence experienced by care teams can create high levels of stress and fear amongst health/social care professionals. This can have a long-reaching negative impact upon individuals, the wider team, the service and its culture, and indeed the service user themselves (Royal College of Psychiatrists, 2005). Understanding the impact of working with the potential for, threat of and actual violence is essential in providing safe, effective and therapeutic services.

Working with aggressive and violent situations

Working with violent offenders with learning disabilities is likely to involve hostile, aggressive and threatening behaviour that may or may not result in violent behaviour. In many situations, there is a potential for early recognition and the implementation of intervention strategies that can be used in an effort to safely manage and de-escalate such behaviour.

Due to the impact of anger and arousal on information processing and decision-making, earlier intervention strategies are likely to be more successful in achieving a safe resolution. It is essential, therefore, that changes in the presentation of the service user are observed and recognised in order to allow for a proactive response from the care team. Key changes to look out for include:

- changes in physical presentation – facial expression, posture, rapid breathing
- changes in physical activity – restlessness, agitation, pacing, searching for weapons
- changes in communication – increased volume, aggressive, withdrawn
- changes in levels of interaction – invading personal space, isolation.

A proactive response to these changes allows the staff team to develop in confidence and form partnerships that support the service user to use problem-solving skills and communication to resolve difficulties.

De-escalation is also a key component in the prevention of violence, and one that relies on effective communication skills. The provision of training in de-escalation is essential for all staff working with service users who have a history of violence. Examples of key de-escalation strategies for offenders with learning disabilities include:

- ensuring the service user feels listened to by trying to establish and thereby acknowledge the reason for their anger/aggression
- awareness of comprehension and communication difficulties (Blumenthal & Lavender, 2000) that are likely to be exacerbated when the person is aroused
- ensuring that one member of staff takes the lead in communication (in the presence of additional staff where necessary for safety) and that short and simple sentences are used.

Additional key points in the prevention and management of aggression include:

- body language (aim for safety, open and non-threatening)
- tone and volume of voice
- presenting as calm and in control, with a genuine wish to help the service user resolve the situation.
- use of eye contact can be emotive either way (ie. someone with ASD may feel threatened by too much eye contact when feeling aggressive; yet to avoid eye contact completely can make the care staff appear aloof and not interested)
- establish anything hazardous to the situation, such as the use of alcohol and/or illicit substances; this should be established as soon as possible as it will have a direct impact on communication and possible pharmacological intervention.

If de-escalation does not prove effective and the threat of or actual violence remains, the care team will need to consider reactive strategies in order to prevent actual or further violence. Consideration of such strategies should range from the least intrusive (ie. verbal request, taking control for the person, which may necessitate medication and/or a move to a safe, quiet area) through to physical relocation (using approved restraint techniques to a safe, quiet area, an intensive care area or seclusion if necessary/available). It is important for all teams working with violent offenders to have a clear protocol for managing violence, which is based on their own organisational policies and the individual needs presented by the service user.

An important consideration when managing long-term risk of violence is that of maintaining vigilance. For some individuals, the risk of violence will remain static or shift only slowly, and must be managed for extended periods of time through close monitoring by staff. This can be a particular issue for opportunistic offenders. In such cases, staff can quickly become blasé about the risks, as the monitoring becomes tedious and there is no overt violence. In such cases, staff can experience 'vigilance fatigue' and cease to maintain adequate monitoring. At these times, risk management plans are less likely to be implemented adequately and therefore the risk of violence increases. Multidisciplinary teams need to be aware of this and work closely together to find ways of overcoming this problem.

Of course, there are some individuals who can present with unpredictable, sudden, explosive aggression. This is in its essence extremely challenging to predict and difficult to manage. In these instances, it is paramount that the residential assessment/treatment areas are competently staffed and resourced. It can be particularly beneficial to have access to a separate area (such as an intensive care suite) that the service user can access to receive care and minimise further aggression and/or violence.

Pharmacological intervention

Pharmacological agents can have a helpful role in the immediate or short-term management of violence in clinical settings such as hospital wards. They can be used for time-limited periods to manage high arousal or aggression, or for emergency sedation on an as-required basis.

Care must always be taken with the use of PRN (*pro re nata* or 'as required') medication. It is all too easy for this to be used indiscriminately and regularly. It is important to regularly review not only what PRN medication is being prescribed, but also the indications for its use and how much is actually being administered. Clinicians responsible for taking the decision to administer PRN medication need to be able to consider the appropriate route of administration (oral, intramuscular or intravenous), and how to monitor, recognise and treat side effects. In order to do this effectively, access to appropriate clinical equipment is essential and should be directed by local policies as outlined in by NICE (NICE, 2005).

It is best practice to incorporate the use of such medication as part of a more global, holistic care plan about how to manage violence and aggression. Normally, such medication should be used only when nursing, social, and psychological interventions are ineffective. They must never be used a means to punish an individual once violence has occurred.

Impact on the individual

Any service user or member of the care team who suffers injury during an adverse incident must always receive immediate medical attention. It is equally important, however, that the longer reaching psychological impact is acknowledged and addressed. The issue of pressing criminal charges against the service user is a contentious and difficult decision for any care professional who has been assaulted. It may feel in direct conflict with the therapeutic relationship, where carers strive to build and maintain effective therapeutic alliances with service users. This is particularly difficult if the victim has ongoing contact with the service user (which is generally the case), but should not be a reason to forego legal proceedings. In these cases, the employing organisation has a responsibility to provide appropriate support. Conversely, the service user who has threatened or acted violently can experience heightened distress and even post-traumatic stress as a result of their actions. For those affected by the incident, there will be a need for a post-incident strategy that deals with both service user and staff reaction. This will include support through interaction and debriefing. For some, there may also be a need for additional support.

Conclusion

Working with violent offenders presents significant challenges to clinical teams and organisations. This is due not only to the complex needs of this client group but also to the impact of violent behaviour on direct care staff and fellow service users. Working and living with the threat of and actual violence can have significant negative effects on the functioning of clinical teams and organisations unless the appropriate support systems are in place. Furthermore, in order to be able to provide a safe and effective service for violent offenders, services and organisations must ensure adequate training is provided for direct care staff in the prevention and management of violence. In this context, clinical teams can then begin to explore the myriad of factors leading to the development and maintenance of violent behaviour and deliver multifaceted intervention programmes whilst ensuring adequate risk management strategies are in place. The effectiveness of any risk management approach lies not only in the availability of detailed information and ongoing evaluation, and the updating of risk management plans, but also in the communication of this to direct care staff along with communication about the rationale underlying intervention and management plans to ensure consistent and safe service delivery.

References

Allan R, Lindsay WR, MacLeod F & Smith AHW (2001) Treatment of women with intellectual disabilities who have been involved with the criminal justice system for reasons of aggression. *Journal of Applied Research in Intellectual Disabilities* **14** 340-347.

Benson B (1994) Anger management training: A self-control program for people with mild mental retardation. In: N Bouras (Ed) *Mental Health in Mental Retardation* (pp224-232). Cambridge: Cambridge University Press.

Bishop AJ & Henry JC (2008) The assessment and treatment of a man with mild learning disability, violent behaviour and chronic low self-esteem: a case study. *Advances in Mental Health in Learning Disabilities* **2** (1) 38-44.

Blumenthal S & Lavender T (2000) *Violence and Mental Disorder: A critical aid to the assessment and management of risk*. London: Jessica Kingsley.

Harris J, Allen D, Cornick M, Jefferson A & Mills R (1996) *Physical Intervention: A policy framework*. Kidderminster: BILD/NAS.

Harris J, Cornick M, Jefferson A, Mills R & Paley S (2008) *Physical Interventions: a policy framework revised edition*. Kidderminster: BILD/NAS.

Hogue T, Steptoe L, Taylor JL, Lindsay WR, Mooney P, Pinkney L, Johnston S, Smith AHW & O'Brien G (2006) A comparison of offenders with intellectual disability across three levels of security. *Criminal Behaviour and Mental Health* **16** 13-28.

Kay SR, Wolkenfeld F & Murrill L (1988) Profiles of aggression amongst psychiatric in patients; I. nature and prevalence. *Journal of Nervous and Mental Disease* **176** (9) 539-546.

Lindsay WR, Allan R, MacLeod F, Smart N & Smith AHW (2003) Long-term treatment and management of violent tendencies in men with intellectual disabilities convicted of assault. *Mental Retardation* **92** 492-501.

National Institute for Clinical Excellence (2005) *Violence – The short-term management of disturbed/ violent behaviour in psychiatric inpatient settings and emergency departments*. London. NICE

Novaco RW (1994a) *Novaco Anger Scale and Provocation Inventory (NAS-PI)*. Los Angeles, CA: Western Psychological Services.

Novaco RW (1994b) Anger as a risk factor among the mentally disordered. In: J Monahan and HJ Steadman (Eds) *Violence and Mental Disorder: Developments in Risk Assessment* (pp 21-59). Chicago: University of Chicago Press.

O'Neill RE, Horner RH, Albin RW, Storey K & Sprague JR (1997) *Functional Assessment and Program Development for Problem Behavior: A practical handbook* (2nd edition). Pacific Grove, CA: Brooks/ Cole.

Taylor JL (2002) A review of the assessment and treatment of anger and aggression in offenders with intellectual disability. *Journal of Intellectual Disability Research* **46** (Supplement 1) 57-73.

Taylor JL & Novaco RW (2004) Assessment of anger and aggression in male offenders with developmental disabilities. *Psychological Assessment* **16** (1) 42-50.

Taylor JL, Novaco RW, Gillmer BT, Robertson A & Thorne I (2005) Individual cognitive-behavioural anger treatment for people with mild-borderline intellectual disabilities and histories of aggression: a controlled trial. *British Journal of Clinical Psychology* **44** 367-384.

Taylor JL, Novaco RW, Gilmer B & Thorne I (2002) Cognitive-behavioural treatment of anger intensity among offenders with intellectual disabilities. *Journal of Applied Research in Intellectual Disabilities* **15** 151-165.

Tyrer P, Oliver-Africano PC, Ahmed Z, Bouras N, Cooray S, Deb S, Murphy D, Hare M, Meade M, Reece B, Kramo K, Bhaumik S, Harley D, Regen A, Rao B, North B, Eliahoo J, Karatela S, Soni A & Crawford M (2008) Risperidone, haloperidol and placebo in the treatment of aggressive challenging behaviour in patients with intellectual disability: a randomised control trial. *Lancet* **371** 57-63.

Royal College of Psychiatrists (1998) *Management Of Imminent Violence: Clinical guidelines to support mental health services* (Occasional Paper Op41). London: Royal College Of Psychiatrists.

Royal College Of Psychiatrists (2005) *The Evidence Base for the Management of Imminent Violence in Learning Disability Settings* (Occasional Paper Op57). London: Royal College of Psychiatrists.

Section 4
Part D

Risk assessment and management

Eddie Chaplin, Enid Grennan and Helen Philp

Introduction

This chapter considers risk assessment, from both practical and clinical perspectives, for people with learning disabilities who use secure and other forensic services. The current evidence base and the clinical utility for risk assessment measures are also considered, along with issues of risk assessment in everyday clinical practice.

Growth of risk assessment

Prior to the introduction of risk assessment, the dangerousness of the individual was the key consideration for clinicians. The term 'dangerousness' eventually became outdated, as it implied a static state that was unlikely to change. This is in contrast to the philosophy of risk assessment, where there is an acknowledgement that people can change over time and may be open to interventions that may reduce risk to themselves and/or others.

Following a number of highly publicised cases and inquiries involving mentally disordered offenders, risk assessment has been promoted as both a clinical and a public priority within mental health care services (eg. Clunis (Ritchie *et al*, 1994), Stone (Francis *et al*, 2000) and Barratt (NHS London, 2006). The disproportionate media coverage attracted by these and similar cases, and the inquiries that followed, have led to a number of recommendations that have changed how we work with this group. The recommendations have included:

- the need for greater interagency co-operation, to prevent people falling through the net
- a significant increase in security across secure services

These cases have also led to questions being asked about the accuracy of risk assessment (Reed, 1997), across all mental health services, and led to the expectation that mental health professionals can and will make risk assessment judgements in everyday practice.

The Inquiries, together with an increased confidence in risk assessment measures from clinicians, have contributed to risk assessment becoming an integral part of penal, health and social care, not just where there is a likelihood of imminent or long-term violence and/or offending, but in all settings where it is now the norm to routinely assess other criteria such as vulnerability, suicide or self-harm.

Risk assessment and risk management: what are they for and what do they do?

Risk assessment

There are various definitions of risk. Undrill (2007), offers a useful definition for mental health practice: '....risk is the product of a measure of the probability of an event (in psychiatry this is usually a subjective probability) and a measure of the impact of an event. This is the standard use of the term in many professional circles, including psychiatry. Although it can be expressed in numerical terms, in everyday clinical practice the probability is often considered in terms of high, medium or low, as is the combined measure'.

The risk assessment process can be described in four stages:

1. Identify the risk – what are we assessing for? Is it violence? Self-harm?

2. Quantify the risk – when does it occur? How does it occur? How often does it occur?

3. Record and interpret – monitor occurrences of behaviour and both its patterns and its effects. Define possible emergence of new risks.

4. Corroborate the evidence, in particular historical and report-driven data. This is to see if anything has been missed and to ensure the accuracy of reporting (eg. have events been minimised or sensationalised?).

The risk assessment process is therefore designed to identify the hazard(s) or risk(s). From this information, a risk management plan will be devised.

Risk management

Risk management is part of the systematic process designed to manage and reduce risk. It draws upon the available information to devise a plan that will minimise risk to others and self. The plan is usually made up of a range of interventions, and/or provides structures such as support, supervision and restrictions. It can be used to contain the risk and/or test the level of risk in a controlled manner. In testing risk, it should be evident that there is some benefit in taking the risk, but this should not outweigh the possible negative consequences. The challenge is to design a management plan to minimise the likelihood of the behaviour occurring (proactive) and a plan of what to do should it occur unexpectedly or despite intervention (reactive). As with risk assessment, risk management is a team effort and is subject to ongoing evaluation and review.

Methods of risk assessment

A number of methods have been used to measure risk. These include:

- **Case note review and/or personal judgement:** relies on unstructured judgements being made on the available information and is reported to be a poor indicator. Approximately a third of predictions are accurate, indicating that this method is little better than chance. It may consider variables thought, by clinicians, to have some predictive qualities.

- **Actuarial methods:** 'those which predict risk on the basis of grouped statistical data' (Lewis & Webster, 2004). These instruments use mainly static predictors (common exceptions may be variables such as age and previous offences). They have gained credibility for long-term risk prediction for offender populations by providing cut off scores. This allows resources to be targeted towards those thought to be most at risk (eg. Violence Risk Appraisal Guide (VRAG), Quinsey *et al*, 2006).

- **Dynamic prediction:** looks at the 'here and now', and change in particular, in terms of factors that affect the individual, such as environment and the individual's clinical presentation. These measures consider the current context and presentation in order to explore whether these are useful in predicting short-term risk.

- **Clinical and combination measures:** these normally use combinations of static and dynamic factors. One example of a clinical measure to predict risk is the Psychopathy Checklist Revised (PCL-R) (Hare, 2003) originally designed to measure psychopathy. There are a number of other measures that use clinical and actuarial measures combined (eg. Historical Clinical Risk (HCR-20) (Webster *et al*, 1997).

- **Iterative Classification Tree (ICT):** devised by Monahan *et al* (2001). A method tree that allows different combinations of risk factors to be considered. The questioning focuses on the individual's risk and the focus of the assessment changes depending on the individuals' previous answers, rather than using a predetermined set of questions.

Risk assessment instruments in clinical practice

There have been a number of risk assessment measures used with offenders with learning disabilities. Below is a selection of established and piloted measures that have been used with learning disabilities populations. (The variables used to predict within the HCR-20, VRAG, PCL-R, STATIC-99 and RRASOR are shown in **Table 4D.2** on page 144.)

- **Historical Clinical Risk management-20 (HCR-20)**
  Webster *et al*, 1997

  The HCR-20 is designed to measure violent behaviour in individuals with mental disorder. It has three sections. The historical section (H) is a 10-item list that assesses previous behaviour and experiences. The PCL-R is included in this section as a measure of psychopathy. The clinical section (C) is a five-item list that assesses the current clinical picture and what risks might arise from it. Finally, risk management (R) is another five-item list, which speculates on how the individual might fare. These R factors change, for example, with the degree of co-operation and support networks available or accepted. Each of the 20 items is given score of 0, 1 or 2. Rather than being a concrete indicator of risk, the final score (along with the other information collected) is a good indicator of who is most likely to pose a risk.

- **Violence Risk Appraisal Guide (VRAG)**
  Quinsey *et al*, 2006

  The VRAG is an actuarial instrument that is designed to assess the likelihood of violent reoffending. Its main strength is its predictive accuracy across populations. The VRAG uses a score of between 0 and 100, which indicates the risk of violent reoffending. As with the HCR-20, the final score should only be used as an aid to clinical judgement, rather than replacing it. There are examples (such as Harold Shipman) that show that final scores are not always an accurate reflection; although unique and atypical, these cases serve as a warning that the final score may not always indicate the individual's risk.

- **Dynamic Risk Assessment and Management System (DRAMs)**
  Lindsay *et al*, 2004

  The DRAMS is a dynamic risk predictor, which has been used in a high security learning disability population. Lindsay *et al* (2004) reported that four variables in the measure showed promising reliability: mood, psychotic symptoms, self-regulation and compliance with the routine.

- **Psychopathy Check List (PCL-R)**
  Hare, 2003

  The PCL-R was not designed as a measure of risk but as a clinical rating scale, designed to measure psychopathy. More recently, the PCL-R has been used to measure risk, particularly violent recidivism. The PCL-R consists of 20 items, 18 of which are divided into two factors (factor 1, 'aggressive narcissism' and factor 2, 'socially deviant lifestyle'). These are rated on a three-point scale: 0 if the item does not apply at all; 1 if the item applies somewhat; and 2 if the item fully applies. The remaining two items are not directly correlated with either factor. As mentioned earlier, the PCL-R is also used as an indicator within other formal risk assessment measures.

Examples of risk assessment measures specific to sex offending

- **Rapid Risk Assessment of Sexual Reoffending (RRASOR)**
  Hanson & Bussiere, 1998

  This relies on four variables:
  - prior sex offences
  - young age

- male victims
- unrelated victims.

The RRASOR has been used in learning disability populations. Its routine use was reported by Harris and Tough (2004) as the static measure of choice within York Central Hospital's Behavioural Management Services, where it is used to predict risk and assign learning disabled offenders to one of six risk levels. Each of these has associated risk levels regarding future sexual offending. These are stated as percentages at 5-10 years.

- **STATIC-99**
  Hanson & Thornton, 1999

  This is an actuarial measure that consists of 10 items. It is specifically designed to assess the risk of sexual recidivism in males. It is designed to act as a baseline of risk for violent and sexual reconviction from which future risk assessment and management strategies can be implemented.

  The STATIC-99 was created by amalgamating the RRASOR (mentioned above) with the Structured Anchored Clinical Judgement – Minimum (SACJ-Min).

Evidence base for risk assessment in learning disabilities

The evidence base on risk assessment for mentally disordered offenders has been developing for over 20 years. Gray *et al* (2007) reported the HCR-20 as being a significant predictor of violence in people with learning disabilities, without the need for modification, in spite of longer spells between offending in this group. More recently, the HCR-20, VRAG and STATIC-99 were used in a study by Lindsay *et al* (2008), across three levels of security (L1 high secure; L2 medium and low secure; and L3 community forensic). The study reported that both the HCR-20 and VRAG showed an orderly pattern, with L1 scoring higher than L2, which scored higher than L3. The HCR-20 showed significant scores across this pattern, whilst the VRAG achieved significance between L1 and L3. With regard to the prediction of incidents, the HCR-20 and VRAG reported significant values for violence prediction, as did the STATIC-99 for sexual risk. With risk assessment research into this area still in its infancy, there have been mixed results. Quinsey *et al* (2004), found that the VRAG, did not have the predictive validity of earlier VRAG studies, in other offender populations, although the findings were much better than chance.

In a study of 73 offenders with learning disabilities in a high-secure hospital, Morrissey *et al* (2007) found the PCL-R did not perform as well as the HCR-20 in terms of finding evidence to support its ability to predict institutional aggression in people with learning disabilities, which is not in keeping with results in other offender samples. In their evaluation of the RRASOR, Harris and Tough (2004) reported that the predictors in this measure appeared equally valid for people with learning disabilities as for other offender populations. The literature thus far seems to suggest that the key to using these measures in practice is to beware of their limitations (McGrath *et al*, 2007). However, it would seem that even those that have shown moderate accuracy with some learning disability offender groups, can be weaved into existing assessment protocols used in clinical settings to give a more reliable estimate of risk.

Problems with risk assessment

It cannot be taken for granted that the risk assessment instruments used in non-learning disabilities populations are valid and reliable for people with learning disabilities. There are a number of reasons why this may be the case, including the lack of normative data for learning disabled offenders, the higher prevalence of mental health problems in learning disabled populations (Gitta & Goldberg, 1995; Stavrakaki & Mintsioulis, 1997; Cooper *et al*, 2007) and the lack of applicability of some of the areas covered in risk assessment measures (such as employment, independent living and relationships, which may not be valid indicators in learning disability populations who are likely to have different experiences).

The overwhelming majority of risk measures in current use are likely to have been standardised on non-learning disability populations, so a risk assessment measure piloted on inmates within a high security prison may have limited use in other settings. Also, although risk measures are often developed to work across multiple clinical groups, the core risk predictors (such as being a young male, and substance abuse) do not apply across all service groups (eg. elderly care or child and adolescent services). It is arguable that completing a poor risk assessment is worse than no risk assessment. Not only can a poor risk assessment be clinically misleading, it can also have a significant impact on the individual's life. Poor information and conclusions can affect the fine balance between placing restrictions on the person and putting the public at risk.

Although risk assessment should be carried out as part of our professional roles, there may be times when personal judgements affect this process. For example, underestimating an individual's risk can arise from moral judgement, such as the desire not to see an individual be prosecuted. This may lead to professionals minimising an individual's behaviour, or not checking accuracy of evidence or archival data, leading to an incomplete assessment. In managing risk, clinicians can also overestimate the role of interventions, for example believing a treatment change such as a change in drug therapy will extinguish future risk, or having unrealistic timescales in which to see improvements.

In contrast, overestimation of risk can lead to unnecessary restrictions of an individual's liberty. This can occur if an individual's behaviour is interpreted out of context or is poorly tolerated by clinicians (although it may be an anticipated risk, which is planned for within current guidelines). This may lead to calls for the person to face sanctions (eg. withdrawal of activities), undermining both the care plan and the need for a systematic approach. Another problem is that staff teams may become blasé after having worked with an individual for a number of years. In losing their clinical focus, they may determine the person's risk without challenging or reviewing the evidence.

The predictive accuracy of clinical decisions is often talked about in terms of true and false positives and negatives. **Table 4D.1** illustrates this in terms of clinical prediction and outcome.

Table 4D.1: Types of decision outcome

True positives Predicted to be violent? **YES** Violence occurred? **YES**	**False positives** Predicted to be violent? **YES** Violence occurred? **NO**
False negatives Predicted to be violent? **NO** Violence occurred? **YES**	**True negatives** Predicted to be violent? **NO** Violence occurred? **NO**

Day-to-day practice informing risk assessment and managing risks

In order to provide support, supervision and treatment safely, risk assessment and management strategies need to be an integral part of an individual's care package. Risk assessment within clinical settings is a dynamic process based upon ongoing observation and assessment by the clinical team working with the person. This informs both day-to-day management and proactive strategies aimed at minimising risk. For example, Mr A always experiences low mood around the anniversary of his index offence that led to his mother's death. This leads to him becoming less communicative, a deterioration in his self-care and possible refusal to eat and/or drink, accompanied by thoughts about harming himself. It is this type of information that staff need to be aware of and act upon in order to work proactively with Mr A. There should be an awareness of these risks so a care plan can be constructed prior to the anniversary of the offence in order to reduce the likelihood of self-neglect and/or harm.

Monitoring and anticipating

Being able to recognise clinical change and the context in which it occurs is an essential skill in effective risk assessment and management. Consider the following scenarios and what action might need to be taken:

- A person diagnosed with psychosis begins to become unwell. It was in the context of psychosis that previous offences have been committed. What are the early warning signs or indicators of relapse, and how does the care plan reflect this?

- A person with autism is about to experience a change in his routine as, due to a lack of staff, he will not be able to attend his usual local evening activities. Such changes are known to be a trigger to violent or maladaptive behaviour. How can you support the client to manage this change?

- A person with bipolar disorder begins to experience elevated mood 'mania'. What changes do you notice? For example, does his ability to concentrate change? Is he spending excessive amounts of money, expressing grandiose thoughts and, most alarmingly, becoming more sexually disinhibited? How do you respond to this?

Not being able to meet requests immediately is a theme seen both in hospital and in the community, and is often cited as a trigger of incidents. Is it possible to anticipate what type of requests will be made and plan to facilitate those that are feasible? If not, can alternatives be offered? When the request has to be denied, what is the best way to communicate this?

In order to be able to effectively implement risk management strategies, clinical teams need to be able to communicate effectively. The clinical information gained from the risk assessment process will inform risk management. A lack of communication or the communication of inaccurate information can increase risk to service users, staff and the public. Communication in this context is the sharing of information to enhance the risk assessment process. It may happen at predetermined times of day or as and when appropriate, such as:

- during handover between shifts
- post-session, following individual work with the person
- after community trips
- between agencies working with the person (eg. health, social services, local authority housing).

One of the most common ways in which services assess risk is by the gradual development of activities in terms of trust and independence; for example, leave in hospital grounds and/or in the community, reduction in supervision and increasing independence in daily living skills. This step-by-step approach allows clinical teams to assess how the patient copes at each of the stages. However, certainly in the early stages (and for some in the long-term), this involves some degree of supervision and support, working alongside the individual.

The following is an example of how risk assessment and management can be incorporated into day-to-day practice. Once it is deemed safe to engage in prescribed activities, there needs to be a fuller more global assessment. Prior to embarking on such activities, the following need to be considered:

1. Undertake a brief assessment of the person's current presentation in line with risk assessment and triggers. With this in mind, consider whether the environment and the activity is safe, and whether the activity needs to be adapted to assist safe engagement.

2. Clearly define the boundaries of the session, including what you are going to do, where the activity will take place, how long it will take to do, how you will get there, who else will be involved etc.

3. Outline your expectations of the person and what they will be responsible for (ie. if going out to a cafe for tea, who will pay for the tea), what is expected in terms of behaviour (ie. to let you know if they become distressed, to give other people personal space, not to pester people for goods or provisions).

4. Ensure the planned activity is within the person's current care plan and identify contingencies for if the activity needs to be changed. (Update of Section 17 forms for those detained under the Mental Health Act).

5. Have a good understanding of the person's skills. For example, being verbally fluent does not always mean that they have practical skills such as money management. If you know the level of support a client needs, you will avoid potentially humiliating/distressing them by offering too much or too little support, and will therefore reduce the likelihood of risk behaviour occurring if it is related to those triggers.

As an example of a more specific activity, the 'kitchen sessions' scenario that follows illustrates some of the issues when risk assessing activities for clients in the kitchen, and provides an example not only of general considerations for sessions but also of how we can consider risk within therapy sessions. This is not an exhaustive list and staff will need to consider the needs of individual service users according to what the service allows and can offer in terms of supervision.

- Before the session, check the kitchen is ready to be used.
- Before introducing a person to cooking with others, undertake some individual sessions so that you have an understanding of their skills. It may be that some people will always need to cook on an individual basis.
- Check the person's mental state. Are they impulsive? Is it safe to boil water or use the hobs? If not, the session does not have to end but it may need to be adapted to minimise or prevent use of items that might be hazardous.
- Ensure the person is aware of the procedures relating to items that may be seen as potential weapons. For example, are sharps counted before and after sessions? Is only one sharp allowed out at a time? Adapt the session to take account of the individual's abilities so if it is not appropriate to have sharps, ensure they are locked away and either prepare ingredients beforehand or choose recipes that do not need sharps.
- If the person is able to use sharps, consider initially limiting access and introducing them slowly to sessions.
- Can the person manage working with hot hobs and ovens? If not, are there alternatives (ie. microwave popcorn, dishes that don't require cooking such as sandwiches, or dishes that can be cooked by others later).
- How long will it take to cook the chosen dish? Will the service user be able to engage for that length of time? Can recipes be adapted to use some convenience foods to speed up the process?
- Does the service user need the dish to be perfect or can they tolerate an unknown outcome? For some, a familiar dish is preferable to a new or experimental dish.
- Staff need to be able to tolerate service users having different cooking styles and recipes. There needs to be a balance between choice, safety and learning new skills.

It is not only when completing activities that risk is assessed. There are other scenarios that will require ongoing risk assessment. For example, the following are some of the things that may need to be assessed and/or considered when the person has leave or a pass within the grounds or local area:

- the need for escorts and, if so, how many
- the need for protection (eg. safety alarm) for the staff or person using their pass, should they be unescorted
- whether there is access to any vulnerable groups (eg. children or those less able)
- determine what the person is allowed to take with them
- check the person's clothes on leaving the unit (eg. if they are wearing three jumpers or other clothing they can use to change their appearance, it may indicate an absconding risk); this is also useful to give details of the person's appearance should anything untoward happen (such as absconding)
- whether the person has just enough money for the purpose of the trip or enough to do other activities (eg. abscond, buy drugs and/or alcohol) that are not planned
- whether the person's mental state and behaviour has remained stable since the decision to grant leave was completed
- whether leave is being used appropriately (eg. the person is returning on time, and is not returning with contraband items).

This type of assessment often becomes second nature to those with experience. Nevertheless, there should be a record of the assessment procedure and the outcomes so that progress can be charted. There is also the need for reactive and proactive strategies if the clinical picture changes. Potential adverse outcomes should be considered by the team at the point of assessment, and there should be strategies to change the management plan if these occur. There also needs to be a preferred plan if something happens while the person is out. The care plan may make reference to some of the following strategies:

- reminding them of responsibilities, what we are here for
- prompting them to use coping strategies
- distracting them and moving their attention away from the potential risk
- removal of the person from the situation
- calling for assistance (eg. police).

This list of considerations is not exhaustive. Each situation or type of leave is different; for example, home leave may require additional considerations.

These are examples of a systematic and proactive side to our practice, which also allows transparency. This enables people from outside to audit and ensure quality, with practice based upon the evidence generated from the individual rather than subjective opinion.

Conclusion

We have seen that there has been a growth in risk assessment in forensic learning disability practice. The majority of measures that have been used for people with learning disabilities have been adapted from mainstream forensic practice, although there have been measures designed for and used within specific learning disability populations (eg. high security).
In spite of a growing confidence in formal measures, however, there still needs to be an awareness of risk assessment and management issues in day-to-day practice, and of how this fits into the overall assessment.

A word on training

Using risk measures will normally require official training to be made available for individuals and groups. Alternatively, in-house training and supervision in the use of these measures can be provided by experienced practitioners until competence is achieved.

Completing assessments without training can lead individuals to interpret the statements and questions in different ways. When the interpretation of the questions involved in assessment differs from one person to the next, it can affect the results of the assessment. In addition, there may be poor understanding of what to assess, what to include and what information is needed to make the assessment.

There is enormous potential for error if these measures are used without adhering to the appropriate protocol and guidance, and this can have significant implications for the individual.

Table 4D.2 shows the variables contained within the key risk assessment instruments.

In no way are the lists in Table 4D.2 intended to be reproduced or used to make clinical judgements without the proper training.

Table 4D.2: The variables used to predict within the PCL-R, HCR-20, VRAG, RRASOR and STATIC-99

PCL-R	HCR-20	VRAG	RRASOR
Factor 1: Personality 'aggressive narcissism' • Glibness/superficial charm • Grandiose sense of self-worth • Pathological lying • Conning/manipulative • Lack of remorse or guilt • Shallow affect • Callous/lack of empathy • Failure to accept responsibility for own actions **Factor 2: Case history 'socially deviant lifestyle'** • Need for stimulation/ proneness to boredom • Parasitic lifestyle • Poor behavioural control • Promiscuous sexual behaviour • Lack of realistic, long-term goals • Impulsivity • Irresponsibility • Juvenile delinquency • Early behaviour problems • Revocation of conditional release **Traits not correlated with either factor** • Many short-term marital relationships • Criminal versatility	Historical items **H** **1.** Previous violence **2.** Young age at first violent incident **3.** Relationship stability **4.** Employment problems **5.** Substance use problems **6.** Major mental illness **7.** Psychopathy **8.** Early maladjustment **9.** Personality disorder **10.** Prior supervision failure Clinical items **C** **1.** Lack of insight **2.** Negative attitudes **3.** Active symptoms of major mental illness **4.** Impulsivity **5.** Unresponsive to treatment Risk **R** **1.** Plans lack feasibility **2.** Exposure to destabilisers **3.** Lack of personal support **4.** Non-compliance with remediation attempts **5.** Stress	**1.** Psychopathy checklist (PCL-R) score +VE **2.** Elementary school maladjustment +VE **3.** DSM-III diagnosis of personality disorder +VE **4.** Age at index offence -VE **5.** Lived with both parents to 16 -VE (except for death of parent) **6.** Failure on prior conditional release +VE **7.** Non-violent offence score +VE **8.** Marital status +VE **9.** DSM-III diagnosis of schizophrenia -VE **10.** Victim injury -VE **11.** History of alcohol abuse +VE **12.** Female victim -VE	• Prior sex offences • Young age • Male victims • Unrelated victims **STATIC-99:** **1.** Prior sex offences **a.** charges **b.** convictions **2.** Prior sentencing dates **3.** Any convictions for non-contact sex offenses **4.** Index non-sexual violence **5.** Prior non-sexual violence **6.** Any unrelated victims **7.** Any stranger victims **8.** Any males victims **9.** Young **10.** Single

In no way is it intended for these lists to be reproduced or used to make clinical judgements without the proper training.

References

Cooper S-A, Smiley E, Morrison J, Williamson A & Allan L (2007) Mental ill health in adults with learning disabilities: prevalence and associated factors. *British Journal of Psychiatry* **190** 27-35.

Francis R, Higgins J & Cassam E (2000) *Report of the Independent Inquiry into the Care and Treatment of Michael Stone*. Horley: South East Coast Strategic Health Authority (formerly West Kent Health Authority).

Gitta MZ & Goldberg B (1995) Dual diagnosis: psychiatric and physical disorders in a clinical sample, Part II. *Clinical Bulletin of Developmental Disabilities Programme* **6** 1-2.

Gray NS, Fitzgerald S, Taylor J, MacCulloch MJ & Snowden RJ (2007) Predicting future reconviction in offenders with intellectual disabilities: The predictive efficacy of VRAG, PCL-SV, and the HCR-20. *Psychological Assessment* **19** 474-479.

Hanson RK & Bussiere MT (1998) Predicting relapse: a meta-analysis of sexual offender recidivism studies. *Journal of Consulting and Clinical Psychology* **66** 348-362.

Hanson RK & Thornton D (1999) *Static-99: Improving actuarial risk assessments for sex offenders* (User report No. 1999-02). Ottawa: Department of the Solicitor General of Canada.

Hare RD (2003) *The Hare Psychopathy Checklist – Revised 2nd Edition Technical Manual*. Toronto: Multi-Health Systems, Inc.

Harris AJR & Tough S (2004) Should actuarial risk assessments be used with sex offenders who are learning disabled. *Journal of Applied Research in Learning Disabilities* **17** 235-241.

Lewis AHO & Webster CD (2004) General instruments for risk assessment. *Current Opinion in Psychiatry* **17** 401-406.

Lindsay WR, Hogue TE, Taylor JL, Steptoe L, Mooney P, O'Brien G, Johnston S & Smith AHW (2008) Risk assessment in offenders with intellectual disability: a comparison across three levels of security. *International Journal of Offender Therapy and Comparative Criminology* **52** (1) 90-111.

Lindsay WR, Murphy L, Smith G, Murphy D, Edwards Z, Chittock C, Greive A & Young SJ (2004) The Dynamic Risk Assessment and Management System: an assessment of immediate risk of violence for individuals with offending and challenging behaviour. *Journal of Applied Research in Learning Disabilities* **17** 267-274.

McGrath RJ, Livingston JA & Falk G (2007) A structured method of assessing dynamic risk factors among sexual abusers with learning disabilities. *American Journal on Mental Retardation* **1122** (3) 221-229.

Monahan J, Steadman H, Silver E, Appelbaum P, Robbins P, Mulvey E, Roth LH, Grisso T & Banks S (2001) *Rethinking Risk Assessment: The MacArthur study of mental disorder and violence*. New York: Oxford University Press.

Morrissey C, Hogue T, Mooney P, Allen C, Johnston S, Hollin C, Lindsay WR &Taylor JL (2007) Predictive validity of the PCL-R in offenders with intellectual disability in a high secure hospital setting: Institutional aggression. *Journal of Forensic Psychology & Psychiatry* **18** 1-15.

NHS London (2006) *Report of the Independent Inquiry into the Care and Treatment of John Barrett*. London: NHS London.

Quinsey VL, Book A & Skilling TA (2004) A follow up of deinstitutionalised men with learning disabilities and histories of anti-social behaviour. *Journal of Applied Research in Learning Disabilities* **17** 243-255.

Quinsey VL, Harris GT, Rice ME & Cormier CA (2006) *Violent Offenders: Appraising and managing risk* (2nd edition). Washington, DC: American Psychological Association.

Reed J (1997) Risk assessment and risk management the lessons from recent inquiries. *British Journal of Psychiatry* **170** (Supp 32) 4-8.

Ritchie J, Dick D & Lingham R (1994) *Report of the Committee of Inquiry into the Care and Treatment of Christopher Clunis*. London: HMSO.

Stravrakaki C & Mintsioulis G (1997) Anxiety disorders in persons with mental retardation: diagnostic, clinical, and treatment issues. *Psychiatric Annals* **27** 182-189.

Undrill G (2007) The risks of risk assessment. *Advances in Psychiatric Treatment* **13** 291-297.

Webster CD, Douglass KS, Eaves D & Hart SD (1997) *HCR-20: Assessing Risk for Violence – Version 2*. Vancouver, BC: Mental Health, Law and Policy Institute, and Forensic Psychiatric Services Commission of British Columbia.

Section 5

Glossaries

Forensic and clinical glossary

Acquiescence	A tendency to acquiescence makes an individual less likely to protest and more likely to answer in the affirmative. The function of this may be to cover up limitations or to seek approval or praise
Acquisitive crimes	Crimes in which things are acquired illegally (eg. theft, robbery)
Acquit	To find a person innocent or not guilty of a charge
Actus reus	The act of committing a crime
Aetiology	Cause
Antecedents	What happened before the observed/targeted behaviour occurred
Appropriate adult (AA)	A person appointed to act on behalf of a vulnerable adult or child when they are being questioned by police. The AA's role is to ensure the person understands the proceedings and their rights. This is a requirement under the Police and Criminal Evidence Act (1984)
Challenging behaviour	'Culturally abnormal behaviour(s) of such intensity, frequency or duration that the physical safety of the person or others is placed in serious jeopardy; or behaviour which is likely to seriously limit or deny access to the use of ordinary community facilities' (Emerson, 2000)
Characteristics	Typical or representative of something or someone
Commissioning	A process whereby services are purchased from health providers to meet the health needs of the local community

Comorbidity	The presence of conditions or disease other than the primary diagnosis, which might affect overall outcomes
Counterfeit deviance	Where someone (particularly someone who commits a sex offence) offends due to lack of knowledge or because they are unaware of the (un)acceptability of their behaviours
Court diversion	A mechanism to transfer mentally disordered offenders from court to receive hospital treatment; commonly the remit of a specialist team working within the court
Criminal justice system (CJS)	The system of organisations (eg. police, courts probation, crown prosecution service) that together make up the system responsible for social control
Crown prosecution service (CPS)	Independent of the police, this service provides evidence for prosecutions, with the criteria that it is in the public interest and there is a realistic chance of a conviction
Custodial sentence	A sentence involving a prison term
Delusion	A false belief not accounted for by the person's cultural or religious background, or level of intelligence. Delusions are real to the person, so are different from *overvalued ideas*, about which the person will have some level of doubt
Destabilising	Where internal or external factors (eg. mental health problem, life events, substance use) may contribute to an individual going back to previous undesired behaviour or actions
Diagnostic overshadowing	Where the assumption is made that the way the person presents is due to their learning disability and therefore part of their normal presentation
Diminished responsibility	A plea where the individual is not held responsible for their actions as, at the time of their action, they were suffering from an 'abnormality of mind'. Diminished responsibility reduces a charge of murder to manslaughter
Feeble mindedness	A category of learning disability under the Mental Deficiency Act (1913)

Fitness to plead — Refers to the individual's capacity to understand the court proceedings as related to them

Formulation — Attempts to offer an explanation or hypothesis of a clinical situation based upon a clinical assessment

Functional analysis — Looks at the relationship between stimulus and response to find out the function of a given behaviour. The response is usually broken down into antecedents, behaviour and consequences (ABC), to aid understanding of the response process

Hallucinations — A false perception in the absence of stimuli. They occur while the person is conscious or awake, and appear real to them. These are different from illusions, which involve misinterpreting stimulus. Hallucinations can occur across all senses (visual, auditory, olfactory, gustatory or tactile). Hallucinations can also be associated with a number of conditions including drug use, mental disorders and neurological disorders

Index offence — The offence of which the patient has been convicted, and which has led to their current detention or conditional discharge. See: www.legalservices.gov.uk/docs/criminal_contracting/mental_health_reviews.pdf (accessed July 2009)

Indictment — The charge

Interrogative suggestibility — 'The extent to which, within a closed social interaction, people come to accept messages communicated during formal questioning, as the result of which their subsequent behaviour response is affected' (Gudjonsson & Clark, 1986). The person is likely to give in to leading questions (yield) and change their responses when pressure is applied during questioning (shift)

Maintaining factors — What the person sees as a desirable outcome or a consequence of their behaviour. This can apply to prosocial or antisocial behaviours

Mens rea — 'The guilty mind'; the knowledge that your actions are wrong

Moral defectives	Defined under the Mental Deficiency Act (1913) as having 'some permanent mental defect coupled with strong vicious or criminal propensities on which punishment had little or no effect'
Negligence	Conduct that falls short of what would be expected of a reasonable person to protect another individual from foreseeable risks of harm
Neurodevelopmental disorders	Characterised by 'an impairment of the growth and development of the brain or central nervous system. They occur in infancy and childhood and include attention deficit hyperactivity disorder (ADHD), autism and autism spectrum disorders, traumatic brain injury, communication, speech and language disorders, genetic disorders such as fragile-X syndrome, Down syndrome, learning disorders and intellectual disability' (Chaplin *et al*, 2008)
Paranoia	Present in a mental disorder where the person has a delusional fear for their safety or well-being
Perpetrator	The person committing the offence
Perpetuate	Events or circumstances that cause behaviour to continue
Precipitates	Something that causes an event
Predispose	An event or condition that makes something more likely
Probation	A non-custodial sentence where the individual is subject to terms and conditions as specified by the court (eg. attend groups, sign in at a police station, attend probation appointments, not to have contract with named individuals). For monitoring, the individual may be tagged
Psychometric assessment	The use of instruments that measure psychological traits such as attitudes and personality
Psychosocial masking	Limits the expression of psychiatric symptoms. This is often caused by limited life experiences. Symptoms include childlike fantasies, and may have a less complex presentation that can lead to severe symptoms being missed

Recklessness	A person's state of mind at the time of committing an offence, where s/he does not care about or consider the possible adverse consequences of their actions
Recidivism	Used to denote the frequency with which a person is detected or arrested, should they commit additional crimes following release from prison for similar crimes
Remand	The detention of an individual before trial or sentencing
Security	**Physical:** 'Provision, maintenance and correct application of appropriate equipment and technology, by appropriately training staff' (eg. fences, locks) **Relational:** 'Formulation of a therapeutic alliance between staff and patients centred in continuing risk assessment and detailed knowledge of the patient. This relies upon the use of personal and professional skills by each member of staff to ensure they support and offer appropriate treatment for patients' **Procedural:** 'Proper application of set procedures, routines and checking' (DH, 2007)
Stabilising	Events that have a positive influence (eg. family support, employment) and make it less likely that an individual will go back to negative actions and/or behaviour etc
Suggestibility	Where an individual is more responsive to suggestions and more likely to be positive towards them. This could have serious consequences if s/he is being formally questioned
Trigger	A stimulus that sets off an action, process, or series of events
Typology	A study of, or the systematic classification of types
Victim	A person against whom a crime is committed
Vigilance fatigue	A state that can arise after excessive observation, where it becomes increasingly difficult for the person observing to maintain observation (and therefore safe practice) as they are likely to lose concentration or control of the task in hand

References

Chaplin E, O'Hara J, Holt G, Hardy S & Bouras N (2008) MHiLD: A model of specialist mental health services for people with learning disabilities. *Advances in Mental Health and Learning Disabilities* **2** (4) 46-50.

Department of Health (2007) *Best Practice Guidance: Specifications for medium security*. London: Department of Health.

Emerson E (2000) *Challenging Behaviour: Analysis and intervention with people with learning difficulties* (2nd edition). Cambridge: Cambridge University Press.

Gudjonsson GH & Clark NK (1986) Suggestibility in police interrogation: A social psychological model. *Social Behaviour* **1** 83-104.

Research glossary

Abstract	Usually found at the beginning of an article, it offers a 'snapshot' of the study, a brief summary of the research, its aims, methods and results
Audit	A process designed to improve clinical outcomes. This is achieved by measuring current outcomes and practices with a view to using the information to improve services
Blinding	A process that prevents researchers and participants from knowing who receives active treatments and who receives a placebo
Case series	A report detailing the care and treatment of a group of individuals
Case study	A report detailing the care and treatment of a individual
Case-control study	Compares a group of people (known as 'cases') who have the disease in question to an 'experimental' group, where possible matched for similarity to the cases in every aspect apart from having the disease
Cohort	A group of people identified by a common factor or characteristic. A cohort study observes a group over time, recording events and changes, and reports on what happened to them
Comorbidity	The presence of one or more disorders (or diseases) in addition to a primary disease or disorder; or the effect of such additional disorders or diseases
Control	The group receiving a placebo or standard treatment, which is compared against the experimental group to test effectiveness of the intervention and/or treatment trialled
Cross-sectional research	Makes an observation at a single point in time (eg. a survey or opinion poll) to offer a snapshot of whatever is being studied at the time of the study

Effectiveness	The degree to which an intervention has a measurable effect on outcomes
Efficacy	The degree to which an intervention improves clinical outcomes
Epidemiology	The study of the health and disease across different populations
Generalisability	Whether the results of a study can be transferred or assumed as relevant to other groups or populations
Hypothesis	A theory being tested as part of a research project
Incidence	The number of times something occurs in a defined population over a specified period of time (eg. number of people with schizophrenia, number of victims of knife crime)
Intervention	Anything meant to bring about change (eg. medication, CBT)
Longitudinal study	A study that looks for correlations between the identified population (eg. people with learning disabilities) and identified variable(s) (eg. prevalence of mental disorder), over a long period of time. This is usual in establishing trends across generations
Methodology	The methods, procedures and techniques that are used in a given research project and that describe how the research is conducted
Normative data	Represents the normal and average scores of a given sample
Observational study	A study where researchers report on events as they happen. This may or may not involve participation
Placebo	A harmless substitute for the real treatment
Population	The group of people being studied (eg. those with red hair, those with hearing deficits, those in London)
Prevalence	The number of people in a given population who have a particular disease or characteristic (eg. the prevalence of people with asthma)

Probability	The chance of an event occurring
Prospective	A prospective study collects data from events as they happen
Qualitative research	Research using observation, which draws on the personal experiences of others
Quantitative research	Research that produces empirical evidence through data collection and so lends itself to statistical analysis to compare outcomes
Randomised controlled trials (RCT)	A method to test an intervention, where participants are randomised into an experimental group (receiving intervention) and a control group (receiving a placebo). Outcomes are measured in both groups to test effectiveness
Retrospective	A retrospective study gathers its information from using past data (ie. after the event has happened)
Systematic review	A review of the literature of a chosen subject to answer a specific question (eg. effectiveness of drug X in people with anxiety)
Variables	Factors that can exist as different amounts or types (eg. gender, age, weight). A **controlled variable** is a variable that has to remain constant during the experiment (eg. dose, speed). A **dependent variable** is the event being studied (eg. violence, levels of symptoms). The **independent variable** is controlled to see if it brings about change to the dependent variable.

Web links

(NB. All links were accessed in August 2009)

Forensic

LD Offenders
(The Care and Treatment of Offenders with a Learning Disability)
www.ldoffenders.co.uk

Forensic Psychiatry Online
http://priory.com/forpsy.htm

Forensic Psychiatry Research Society
www.fprs.org

Information, voluntary, user groups and charitable

Bob the Psychiatric Nurse
http://dspace.dial.pipex.com/bob.dunning/bobthe.htm

British Institute of Learning Disabilities
www.bild.org.uk

Clear Thoughts
www.clearthoughts.info

Depression Alliance
www.depressionalliance.org

Foundation for People with Learning Disabilities
www.learningdisabilities.org.uk

Greater Manchester Probation Trust
www.gm-probation.org.uk/page.asp?text=14

Joseph Rowntree Foundation
www.jrf.org.uk

Learning about Intellectual Disabilities and Health
www.intellectualdisability.info/home.htm

Mencap
www.mencap.org.uk

Mental Health Alliance
www.mentalhealthalliance.org.uk

Mental Health Foundation
www.mentalhealth.org.uk

Mind (for better mental health)
www.mind.org.uk

NACRO
www.nacro.org.uk

National Autistic Society
www.nas.org.uk

National BME Mental Health Network
www.bmementalhealth.org.uk

National Mental Health Development Unit
www.nmhdu.org.uk

People First - A Voice For People With Learning Difficulties
www.peoplefirstltd.com

Prison Reform Trust
www.prisonreformtrust.org.uk

Rethink
www.rethink.org

Sainsbury Centre for Mental Health
www.scmh.org.uk

Victim Support
www.victimsupport.org.uk

Professional groups and unions

British Association of Occupational Therapists and College of Occupational Therapists
www.cot.co.uk

British Psychological Society
www.bps.org.uk

Royal College of Nursing
www.rcn.org.uk

Royal College of Psychiatrists
www.rcpsych.ac.uk

Social Care Institute for Excellence: Social Care Online
www.scie-socialcareonline.org.uk

Unison
www.unison.org.uk

Government and policy

Care Quality Commission
www.cqc.org.uk

Care Services Improvement Partnership
www.csip.org.uk

Crown Prosecution Service
www.cps.gov.uk

Department of Health
www.dh.gov.uk/en/index.htm

Forensic Mental Health Services Managed Care Network (NHS Scotland)
www.forensicnetwork.scot.nhs.uk/learningdisabilities.asp

HM Courts Service
www.hmcourts-service.gov.uk

HM Prison Service
www.hmprisonservice.gov.uk

Home Office
www.homeoffice.gov.uk

Ministry of Justice
www.justice.gov.uk

NHS National Patient Safety Agency
www.npsa.nhs.uk

Valuing People
http://valuingpeople.gov.uk/index.jsp

Youth Justice Board
www.yjb.gov.uk/en-gb

Youth Justice Trust
www.youth-justice-trust.org.uk

International

American Association on Intellectual and Developmental Disabilities
www.aamr.org

American College of Forensic Psychiatry
www.forensicpsychonline.com

Australasian Society for the Study of Intellectual Disability
www.assid.org.au

European Association for Mental Health in Intellectual Disability
www.mhid.org

Forensic Psychiatry Canada
www.forensicpsychiatry.ca/intro.htm

Hooper's Forensic Psychiatry
http://bama.ua.edu/~jhooper

National Association for the Dually Diagnosed (North America)
www.thenadd.org

Psychology Information Online
www.psychologyinfo.com/forensic/

History

Learning Disability History
www.learningdisabilityhistory.com

Mental Health (History) Timeline
http://studymore.org.uk/mhhtim.htm#1842

Best practice guidelines

National Institute for Health and Clinical Excellence
www.nice.org.uk

POVA - Protection of Vulnerable Adults Scheme
www.criminalrecordchecks.co.uk/pova-list.htm

Other

Estia Centre
www.estiacentre.org

Institute of Psychiatry
www.iop.kcl.ac.uk

Jan-net Ltd
www.jan-net.co.uk
(Run by Janet Cobb. Includes a number of networks, including forensic learning disabilities, which are free to join.)

Tizard Centre
www.kent.ac.uk/tizard